BURT FRANKLIN: RESEARCH & SOURCE WORKS SERIES
Science Classics Series 10

THOMAS HARIOT

AND HIS

ASSOCIATES

' chusing always rather to doe some thinge worth
nothing than nothing att all.'   *Sir William Lower
to Hariot* July 19 1611 (see p. 99)

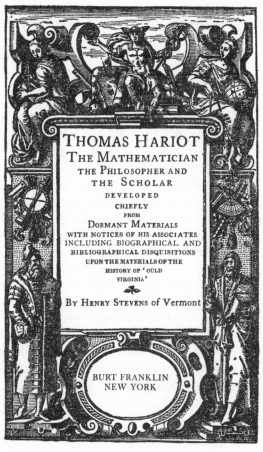

THOMAS HARIOT

The Mathematician

the Philosopher and

the Scholar

DEVELOPED

CHIEFLY

FROM

DORMANT MATERIALS

WITH NOTICES OF HIS ASSOCIATES

INCLUDING BIOGRAPHICAL AND

BIBLIOGRAPHICAL DISQUISITIONS

UPON THE MATERIALS OF THE

HISTORY OF 'OULD

VIRGINIA'

By HENRY STEVENS of Vermont

BURT FRANKLIN
NEW YORK

Published by LENOX HILL Pub. & Dist. Co. (Burt Franklin)
235 East 44th St., New York, N.Y. 10017
Reprinted: 1972
Printed in the U.S.A.

Burt Franklin: Research and Source Works Series:
Science Classics Series: 10

Reprinted from the original edition in the Wesleyan University
    Library.

Library of Congress Cataloging in Publication Data

Stevens, Henry, 1819-1886.
    Thomas Hariot, the mathematician, the philosopher, and the
scholar.

    Reprint of the 1900 ed.
    1. Hariot, Thomas, 1560-1621. I. Title.
F229.H297 1972   510'.92'4 [B]   72-82483
ISBN 0-8337-3399-0

To
FRANCIS PARKMAN
THE
HISTORIAN and TRUSTIE FRIEND
Who Forty Years ago
When we were young Students of History together
Gave me a hand of his over the Sea
NOW
Give I him this right hand of mine
with
Ever grateful Tribute to
our life-long
FRIENDSHIP

Custos juris reimprimendi
Caveat homo trium literarum

[The touching Dedication on the opposite page was penned by my
father a few months before his death on February 28, 1886. I have
thought best to leave it exactly as he had planned it, although now,
alas! Mr. Parkman is no longer with us. Let us hope the old friends
may have again joined hands beyond the unknown sea.—H. N. S.]

EXPLANATORY

I N the year 1877 the late Mr. Henry Stevens of Vermont, under the pseudonym of 'Mr. Secretary Outis,' projected and initiated a literary Association entitled THE HERCULES CLUB. The following extracts from the original prospectus of that year explain his 'platform':

"The objects of this Association are "literary, social, antiquarian, festive and "historical; and its aims are thoroughly "independent research into the materials of "early Anglo-American history and litera-"ture. The Association is known as THE

Explanatory

" HERCULES CLUB, whose Eurystheus is
" Historic Truth and whose appointed la-
" bours are to clear this field for the historian
" of the future.

" Sinking the individual in the Associa-
" tion the Hercules Club proposes to scour
" the plain and endeavour to rid it of some
" of the many literary, historical, chronolo-
" gical, geographical and other monstrous
" errors, hydras and public nuisances that
" infest it. . . . Very many books, maps,
" manuscripts and other materials relating
" alike to England and to America are well
" known to exist in various public and private
" repositories on both sides of the Atlantic.
" Some unique or of the highest rarity, are
" of great historic value, while others are
" difficult of access, if not wholly inaccessible,
" to the general student. It is one of the
" purposes therefore of the Hercules Club to
" ferret out these materials, collate, edit and
" reproduce them with extreme accuracy, but
" not in facsimile. The printing is to be in
" the best style of the Chiswick Press. The
" paper with the Club's monogram in each leaf
" is made expressly for the purpose.".

The following ten works were selected as the first field of the Club's investigations, and to form the first series of its publications.

1. Waymouth (Capt. George) Voyage to North Virginia in 1605. By James Rosier. London, 1605, 4°
2. Sil. Jourdan's Description of Barmuda. London, 1610, 4°
3. Lochinvar. Encouragements for such as shall have intention to bee Vndertakers in the new plantation of Cape Breton, now New Galloway. Edinburgh, 1625, 4°
4. Voyage into New England in 1623-24. By Christopher Levett. London, 1628, 4°
5. Capt. John Smith's True Relation of such occurrences of Noate as hath hapned in Virginia. London, 1608, 4°
6. Gosnold's Voyage to the North part of Virginia in 1602. By John Brereton. London, 1602, 4°
7. A Plain Description of the Barmudas, now called Sommer Islands. London, 1613, 4°
8. For the Colony in Virginia Brittania, Lavves Divine Morall and Martiall, &c. London, 1612, 4°
9. Capt. John Smith's Description of New England, 1614-15, map. London, 1616, 4°
10. Hariot (Thomas) Briefe and true report of the new foundland of Virginia. London, 1588, 4°

'Mr. Secretary Outis' undertook the task of seeing the reprints of the original texts of these ten volumes through the Press, and almost the whole of this work he actually accomplished.

The co-operative objects of the Association, however, appear never to have been fully inaugurated, although a large number of literary

men, collectors, societies and libraries entered
their names as Members of the Club. All
were willing to give their pecuniary support as
subscribers to the Club's publications, but few
offered the more valuable aid of their literary
assistance; hence practically the whole of the
editing also devolved upon Mr. Henry Stevens.

He first took up No. 10 on the above list,
Hariot's Virginia. His long and diligent
study for the introduction thereto, resulted in
the discovery of so much new and important
matter relative to Hariot and Raleigh, that it
became necessary to embody it in the present
separate volume, as the maximum dimensions
contemplated for the introduction to each work
had been exceeded tenfold or more.

Owing to Mr. Stevens's failing health, the
cares of his business, and the continual discovery of fresh material, it was not till 1885
that his investigations were completed, although
many sheets of the book had been printed off
from time to time as he progressed. The
whole of the text was actually printed off
during his lifetime, but unfortunately he did
not live to witness the publication of his work,
perhaps the most historically important of any

of his writings. Publication has since been delayed for reasons explained hereinafter.

On the death of my father, on February 28, 1886, I found myself appointed his literary executor, and I have since devoted much time to the arrangement, completion, and publication of his various unfinished works, seeking the help of competent editors where necessary.

Immediately after his decease I published his *Recollections of Mr. James Lenox of New York, and the formation of his Library*, a little volume which was most favourably received and ran through several impressions.

In the same year I published *The Dawn of British Trade to the East Indies as recorded in the Court Minutes of the East India Company*. This volume contained an account of the formation of the Company and of Captain Waymouth's voyage to America in search of the North-west passage to the East Indies. The work was printed for the first time from the original manuscript preserved in the India Office, and the introduction was written by Sir George Birdwood.

In 1888 I issued *Johann Schöner, Professor of Mathematics at Nuremberg. A reproduction of his Globe of* 1523 *long lost, his dedicatory letter to Reymer von Streytperck, and the ' De Moluccis' of Maximilianus Transylvanus, with new translations and notes on the Globe by Henry Stevens of Vermont, edited, with an introduction and bibliography, by C. H. Coote, of the British Museum.* This Globe of 1523, now generally known as Schöner's Third Globe, is marked by a line representing the route of Magellan's expedition in the first circumnavigation of the earth; and the facsimile of Maximilianus's interesting account of that voyage, with an English translation, was consequently added to the volume. Mr. Coote, in his introduction, gives a graphic account of many other early globes, several of which are also reproduced in facsimile. The whole volume was most carefully prepared, and exhibits considerable originality both in the printing and binding, Mr. Henry Stevens's own ideas having been faithfully carried out.

In 1893 I issued to the subscribers that elegant folio volume which my father always considered as his *magnum opus*. It was entitled *The New Laws of the Indies for the good treatment and preservation of the Indians, promulgated by the*

Emperor Charles the Fifth, 1542-1543. *A facsimile reprint of the original Spanish edition, together with a literal translation into the English language, to which is prefixed an historical introduction.* Of the long introduction of ninety-four pages, the first thirty-eight are from the pen of Mr. Henry Stevens, the remainder from that of Mr. Fred. W. Lucas, whose diligent researches into American history are amply exemplified in his former work, *Appendiculae Historicae, or shreds of history hung on a horn,* and in his recent work, *The Annals of the Voyages of the Brothers Zeno.*

Ever since 1886 I have from time to time unsuccessfully endeavoured to enlist the services of various editors competent to complete the projected eleven volumes of the Hercules Club publications, but after a lapse of nearly fourteen years I have awakened to the fact that no actual progress has been made, and that I have secured nothing beyond the vague promise of future assistance. The field of editors capable of this class of work being necessarily very limited, and death having recently robbed me in the most promising case of even the slender hope of future help, I determined to ascertain for myself the exact position of the work already done, with the hope of bringing at least some of the volumes to a completion separately, instead of waiting longer in the hope of finishing and issuing them all *en bloc* as originally proposed and intended. On collating the printed stock I found that the two volumes, *Hariot's Virginia* and the *Life of Hariot*, were practically complete, the text of both all printed off, and the titles and preliminary leaves and the Index to *Hariot's Virginia* actually standing in type at the Chiswick Press just as my father left them fourteen years ago! (Many thanks to Messrs Charles Whittingham and Co. for their patience.) The proofs of these I have corrected and passed for press, and I have added the Index to the present volume. My great regret is that I did not sooner discover the practical completeness of these two volumes, as owing to the nature of the contents of the *Life of Hariot* it is not just to Hariot's memory, or to that of my father, that such important truths should so long have been withheld from posterity.

These two volumes being thus completed, it

remained to be decided in what manner they should be published. I did not feel myself competent to pick up the fallen reins of the HERCULES CLUB, which, as I have said before, appears never to have been fully inaugurated on the intended co-operative basis. There being now no constituted association (such having entirely lapsed on the death of Mr. 'Secretary Outis'), and many of the original subscribers, who were *ipso facto* members, being also no longer with us, it appeared impossible to put forth the volumes as the publications of the HERCULES CLUB. Consequently I resolved to issue them myself (and any future volumes I may be able to bring to completion) simply as privately printed books, and I feel perfectly justified in so doing, as no one but Mr. Henry Stevens had any hand in their design or production either editorially or financially. No money whatever was received from the members, whose subscriptions were only to become payable when the publications were ready for delivery. The surviving members have been offered the first chance of subscribing to these two Hariot volumes and I am grateful for the support received. They

Explanatory

and the new subscribers will also be offered the option of taking any subsequent volumes of the series which I may be enabled to complete.

HENRY N. STEVENS,

Literary Executor of the late
Henry Stevens of Vermont.

39, Great Russell Street,
   London, W.C.,
     10th February, 1900.

PREMONITION

 HEN I YEARS AGO undertook among other enterprises to compile a sketch of the life of THOMAS HARIOT the first historian of the new found land of Virginia; and to trace the gradual geographical development of that country out of the unlimited 'Terra Florida' of Juan Ponce de Leon, through the French planting and the Spanish rooting out of the Huguenot colony down to the successful foothold of the English in Wingandacoa under

Raleigh's patent, I little suspected either the extent of the research I was drifting into, or the success that awaited my investigations.

The results however are contained in this little volume, which has expanded day by day from the original limit of fifty to above two hundred pages. From a concise bibliographical essay the work has grown into a biography of a philosopher and man of science with extraordinary surroundings, wherein the patient reader may trace the gradual development of Virginia from the earliest time to 1585; ' especially,' says Strachey, ' that which hath bene published by that true lover of vertue and great learned professor of all arts and know-ledges, Mr Hariots, who lyved there in the tyme of the first colony, spake the Indian language, searcht the country,' etc ; Hariot's nearly forty years' intimate connection with Sir Walter Raleigh; his long close companionship with Henry Percy ; his correspondence with Kepler; his participation in Raleigh's 'History of the World ;' his invention of the telescope

and his consequent astronomical discoveries;
his scientific disciples; his many friendships and
no foeships; his blameless life; his beautiful
epitaph in St Christopher's church, and his long
slumber in the 'garden' of the Bank of England.

The little book is now submitted with considerable diffidence, for in endeavouring to extricate
Hariot from the confusion of historical 'facts'
into which he had fallen, and to place him in
the position to which he is entitled by his great
merits, it is desirable to be clear, explicit and
logical. A decision of mankind of two centuries'
standing, as expressed in many dictionaries and
encyclopaedias, cannot be easily reversed without good contemporary evidence. This I have
endeavoured to produce.

Referring to pages 191 and 192 the writer
still craves the reader's indulgence for the
apparently irrelevant matter introduced, as
well as for the inartistic grouping of the many
detached materials, for reasons there given.

It ought perhaps to be stated here that the
book necessarily includes notices, more or less

elaborate, of very many of Hariot's friends, associates and contemporaries, while others, for want of space, are mentioned little more than by name.

The lives of Raleigh, and Henry Percy of Northumberland, Prisoners in the Tower, seem to be inseparable from that of their Fidus Achates, but I have endeavoured to eliminate that of Hariot as far as possible without derogation to his patrons. All the new documents mentioned have their special value, but too much importance cannot be attached to the recovery of Hariot's Will, for it at once dispels a great deal of the inference and conjecture that have so long beclouded his memory. It throws the bright electric light of to-day over his eminently scholarly, scientific and philosophical Life. By this and the other authorities given it is hoped to add a new star to the joint constellation of the honored Worthies of England and America.

HENRY STEVENS of Vermont

Vermont House, xiii Upper Avenue Road,
London, NW, April 10 1885

Thomas Hariot

AND HIS

Associates

OLLECTORS OF RARE
English books always
speak reverently and even
mysteriously of the 'quarto Hariot' as they do of
the 'first folio.' It is given
to but few of them ever to
touch or to see it, for not more than seven copies
are at present known to exist. Even four of
these are locked up in public libraries, whence
they are never likely to pass into private hands.

One copy is in the Grenville Library; another is in the Bodleian; a third slumbers in the University of Leyden; a fourth is in the Lenox Library; a fifth in Lord Taunton's; a sixth in the late Henry Huth's; and a seventh produced £300 in 1883 in the Drake sale.

The little quarto volume of Hariot's Virginia is as important as it is rare, and as beautiful as it is important. Few English books of its time, 1588, surpass it either in typographic execution or literary merit. It was not probably thrown into the usual channels of commerce, as it bears the imprint of a privately-printed book, without the name or address of a publisher, and is not found entered in the registers of Stationers' Hall. It bears the arms of Sir Walter Raleigh on the reverse of the title, and is highly commended by Ralfe Lane, the late Governor of the Colony, who testifies, ' I dare boldly auouch it may very well pass with the credit of truth even amongst the most true relations of this age.' It was manifestly put forth somewhat hurriedly to counteract, in influential quarters, certain slanders and aspersions spread abroad in England by some ignorant persons returned from Virginia, who ' woulde seeme to knowe so much as no men more,' and who ' had little vnderstanding, lesse discretion, and more tongue then was needful or requisite.' Hariot's book is dated at the end, February 1588, that is 1589 by present reckoning. Raleigh's assignment is dated the 7th of March following. It is probable therefore that the 'influential quarters' above referred to meant the Assignment of Raleigh's Charter which would have expired by the limitation of six years on the 24th of March, 1590, if no colonists had been shipped or plantation attempted. It is possible also that Theodore De Bry's presence in London, as mentioned below, may have hastened the printing of the volume.

Indeed, the little book professes to be only an epitome of what might be expected, for near the end the author says, ' this is all the fruits of our labours, that I haue thought necessary to aduertise you of at present;' and, further on, ' I haue ready in a discourse by it self in maner

b

of a Chronicle according to the course of times, and when time shall bee thought conuenient, shall also be published.' Hariot's 'Chronicle of Virginia' among things long lost upon earth! It is to be hoped that some day the historic trumpet of Fame will sound loud enough to awaken it, together with Cabot's lost bundle of maps and journals deposited with William Worthington ; Ferdinand Columbus' lost life of his father in the original Spanish ; and Peter Martyr's book on the first circumnavigation of the globe by the fleet of Magalhaens, which he so fussily sent to Pope Adrian to be read and printed, also lost ! Hakluyt, in his volume of 1589, dated in his preface the 17th of November, gives something of a chronicle of Virginian events, 1584-1589, with a reprint of this book. But there are reasons for believing that this is not the chronicle which Hariot refers to. As White's original drawings have recently turned up after nearly three centuries, may we not still hope to see also Hariot's Chronicle ?

However, till these lost jewels are found let

us appreciate what is still left to us.   Hariot's
'True Report' is usually considered the first original authority in our language relating to that
part of English North America now called the
United States, and is indeed so full and trustworthy that almost everything of a primeval character that we know of ' Ould Virginia' may be
traced back to it as to a first parent.   It is an
integral portion of English history, for England
supplied the enterprise and the men. It is equally
an integral portion of American history, for America supplied the scene and the material.

Without any preliminary flourish or subsequent reflections, the learned author simply and
truthfully portrays in 1585-6 the land and the
people of Virginia, the condition and commodities of the one, with the habits and character of
the other, of that narrow strip of coast lying
between Cape Fear and the Chesapeake, chiefly
in the present State of North Carolina. This
land, called by the natives Wingandacoa, was
named in England in 1584 Virginia, in compliment to Queen Elizabeth.   This name at first

covered only a small district, but afterwards it possessed varying limits, extending at one time over North Virginia even to 45 degrees north.

Raleigh's Virginia soon faded, but her portrait to the life is to be found in Hariot's book, especially when taken with the pictures by Captain John White, so often referred to in the text. This precious little work is perhaps the most truthful, trustworthy, fresh, and important representation of primitive American human life, animals and vegetables for food, natural productions and commercial commodities that has come down to us. Though the ' first colonie ' of Raleigh, like all his subsequent efforts in this direction, was a present failure, Hariot and White have left us some, if not ample, compensation in their picturesque account of the savage life and lavish nature of pre-Anglo-Virginia, the like of which we look for in vain elsewhere, either in Spanish, French, or English colonization.

Indeed, nearly all we know of the uncontaminated American aborigines, their mode of life and domestic economy, is derived from this book, and therefore its influence and results as an original authority cannot well be over-estimated. We have many Spanish and French books of a kindred character, but none so lively and life-like as this by Hariot, especially as afterwards illustrated by De Bry's engravings from White's drawings described below.

The first breath of European enterprise in the New World, combined with its commercial Christianity, seems in all quarters, particularly the Spanish and English, to have at once taken off the bloom and freshness of the Indian. His natural simplicity and grandeur of character immediately quailed before the dictatorial owner of property and civilization. The Christian greed for gold and the civilized cruelty practised without scruple in plundering the unregenerate and unbaptized of their possessions of all kinds, soon taught the Indian cunning and the necessity of resorting to all manner of savage and untutored devices to enable him to cope with his relentless enemies for even restrained liberty and self-preservation; nay, even for very existence,

and this too on his own soil that generously gave
him bread and meat. All these by a self-as-
serted authority the coming European civilizer,
with Bible in hand, taxed with tribute of gold,
labour, liberty, life. This has been the common
lot of the western races.

It is therefore refreshing to catch this mirrored
glimpse of Virginia, her inhabitants, and her resources of primitive nature, before she was con-
taminated by the residence and monopoly of
the white man. It may have been best in the
long run that the European races should dis-
place the aborigines of the New World, but it
is a melancholy reflection upon ' go ye into all
the world and preach the gospel unto every crea-
ture,' that no tribe of American Indians has yet
been absorbed into the body politic. Many a
white man has let himself down into savage life
and habits, but no tribe of aborigines has yet
come up to the requirements, the honours, and
the delights of European civilization. Like the
tall wild grass before the prairie-fire, the aborigi-
nal races are gradually but surely being swept

away by the progress of civilization. Now that they are gone or going the desire to gather real and visible memorials of them is increasing, but fate seems to have swept these also from the grasp of the greedy conqueror. Cortes gathered the golden art treasures of Montezuma and sent them to Charles the Fifth, but the spoiler was spoiled on the high seas, and not a drinking-cup or finger-ring of that western barbaric monarch remains to tell us of his island splendour.

A historical word upon the events that led up to Raleigh's Virginia patent may not be out of place in a bibliographical Life of Hariot. The patent was no sudden freak of fortune but was the natural outgrowth of stirring events. Had it not been allotted to Raleigh it would doubtless soon after have fallen to some other promoter. But Raleigh was the Devonshire war-horse that first snuffed the breeze from afar. He fathered and took upon himself the burden of this new-born English enterprise of Western Planting.

Though unsuccessful himself, Raleigh lifted his country into success more than any other one

man of his time. To this day he is honoured
alike in the old country that gave him birth, and
in the new country to which he gave new life.
His energy, enterprise, and fame are now a part
of England's history and pride, while his disgrace
and death belong to his king. Thomas Hariot
was for nearly forty years his confidential lieutenant throughout his varied career.

From his youth Raleigh had sympathized, like
many intelligent Englishmen, with the Huguenot
cause in France. As early as 1569, at the age of
seventeen, he had been one of a hundred volunteers whom Elizabeth sent over to assist and countenance Coligni. He thus probably became better
acquainted with the great but unsuccessful scheme
of colonizing Florida. At all events the history
of that disastrous French Huguenot colonization
was first published under his auspices, and a
chief survivor, Jacques Le Moyne, became attached to his service and interests. The story is
in brief as follows.

Gaspar de Coligni, Admiral of France, often
in our day called the French Raleigh, was a Pro-

testant, and firm friend of England. One of his captains, Jean Ribault, of Dieppe, also a Protestant, had written an important paper on the policy of preserving peace with Protestant England. That paper, transmitted by the Admiral to England, is still preserved in the national archives. Ribault became the leader of Coligni's preliminary expedition in 1562 into Florida to seek out a suitable place, somewhere between 30° north latitude and Cape Breton, for the discomfited Huguenots to retire to and found a Protestant colony. The previous Brazilian project had already been abandoned as impracticable and unsuccessful.

Hitherto the Spanish Roman Catholic maritime doctrine had been that to see or sail by any undiscovered country gave possession. But the French Protestants, now firmly rejecting the Pope's gift, required occupation in addition to discovery to secure title. Hence Florida at that time, not being occupied by the Spanish, was considered open to the French. Ribault sailed from Havre the 18th of February 1562, taking

c

a course across the Atlantic direct, and, as he
thought, new, making his land fall on the 30th
of April at $29\frac{1}{2}$ degrees ; but Verrazano had in
1524 sailed also direct for Florida, taking a
similar course, with the difference that he started
from Madeira.   Thence coasting northward,
seeking for a harbour, touching at the river of
May, and proceeding up the coast to $32\frac{1}{2}$ degrees, Ribault found a good harbour into which
he entered on the 27th of May, and named it
Port Royal. He was so well pleased with the
country that, perhaps contrary to instructions, he
left a colony of thirty volunteers, under Capt.
Albert de la Pierria, and returned home with the
news, arriving in France, after a quick voyage,
on the 20th of July, 1562.

Ribault, on leaving Port Royal, intended to
explore up the coast to 40°, that is, to the present site of New York, but gives various reasons
for not doing so, one of which was 'the declaration made vnto vs of our pilots and some others
that had before been at some of those places
where we purposed to sayle and have been

already found by some of the king's subjects.'
This little colony of Port Royal, after nearly a
year of danger and privation, built a ship and
put to sea, hoping to reach France. After incredible sufferings, they were relieved by an English ship, which, after putting the feeble on shore,
carried the rest to England, having on board a
French sailor who had come home the previous
year with Ribault. These surviving colonists
were all presented to Queen Elizabeth, and attracted much attention and great sympathy in
England. Some found their way back to France,
while others entered the English service. Thus
England became acquainted with the aim, ob-
ject, success, and failure of the first Florida
(now South Carolina) Protestant French colony.
Thomas Hacket published in London the 30th
of May 1563, Ribault's 'True and last Discouerie of Florida,' purporting to be a translation from the French ; but no printed French
original is now known to exist.

The year of bigotry, 1563, in France having
passed, a second expedition of three vessels under

Réné de Laudonnière, who had been an officer
under Ribault in 1562, sailed for Florida from
Havre, April 22, 1564, and arrived at the river
of May the 25th of June. There were men of
courage and consequence in this company of
adventurers, among whom was Le Moyne, the
painter and mathematician. The story of the
sufferings of this second colony has often been
told, and need not be repeated here. Suffice it
to say that it was greatly relieved in July
1565, by Captain John Hawkins on his return
voyage from his second famous slave expedition
to Africa and the West Indies. Hawkins, after
generously relieving the French with food, general supplies, and friendly counsel, returned to
Devonshire, sailing up the coast to Newfoundland, and thence home, bringing stores of gold,
silver, pearls, and the usual valuable merchandize of the Indies, but the store of information
respecting Florida and our Protestant friends,
and especially the geography of the American
coast, was worth more to England than all his
vast store of merchandize.

In 1565 a third French expedition was fitted out, again under Ribault, to supply, reinforce, and support Laudonnière. After many disappointing and vexatious delays, Ribault, late in the season, put to sea, but by stress of weather was forced into Portsmouth, where he remained a fortnight. This gave England still more information respecting the French Protestant projects of southern colonization, as well as of Florida, which at that time extended very far north of its present limits. At length on the 14th of June Ribault left the hospitable shores of England with a fair north east wind to waft his seven ships, freighted with above three hundred colonists including sailors and soldiers, and taking the new ' French route' north of the Azores and south of Bermuda, entered the river of May on the 27th of August, just one month after the departure of Hawkins, and juſt one day before the arrival of the Spaniards at the river of St John, a few miles south.

We find no hint of any opposition in England to these French colonizing schemes, but on the contrary they were looked upon as an advantageous barrier to Spanish greed of territorial extension northward under the vicegerent's gift.

There are still existing hints of English projects of western voyages at this time, about the year 1565, to the American coast. Elizabeth, however, was friendly to the Huguenots, and evinced great sympathy with their Florida colonial scheme. England's claim to Newfoundland and Labrador, through discovery by the Cabots, had been allowed to lapse chiefly from the Protestant doctrine of non-occupation. The French occupation of Canada was not disputed. There was some doubt, however, about the intermediate country between the New France of Canada and the New France of Florida, and hence we find that private plans of English occupation were hatching at this early period, but they were not encouraged. This delicate question between France and Spain was, however, soon settled by the well known course of events with which England had nothing to do but to stand aside till the contest was over, and then in due course of time, like an independent powerful neutral, step in and reap the rewards.

It is well known that Laudonnière's followers were not altogether harmonious. Some restless spirits seceded, and seizing one of the colony's ships, entered successfully in the autumn and winter of 1564-65 into piracy on the rich commerce of Spain in the West Indies. These French spoliations had been a sore point with the owners of West India commerce since the days of Verrazano, so much so that the Spanish Government had instituted a fleet of coastguards among the islands to intercept and destroy the pirates. This fleet for some time had been under the charge of an experienced, trusted, and efficient officer named Pedro Menendez de Avilés. No doubt the provocation was great, and the new piracy was not to be endured. The home government of Spain had been kept informed of the Huguenot encroachments in Florida, a country which had long ago been granted to Ponce de Leon, Ayllon and others, and had been coasted by Estevan Gomez, but these en-

croachments had hitherto been so long winked
at that the French colonists began to feel themselves to be in tolerable security.

French piracy and Calvinism, however, coming together were two provocations too much for
the patriotism and piety of the zealous Roman
Catholic Spanish commander in the West Indies. Besides, there was a sorrow which roused
his Spanish bigotry and induced him more than
ever to serve God and his king by exterminat-
ing heresy. Don Pedro, with his new honors
and high hopes, had left Cadiz on the 31st of
May 1564, as Captain-General of the West
India, the Terra Firma, the Peruvian, and the
New-Spain fleets, his son under him commanding
the ships to Vera Cruz. This son on the home-
ward voyage in the autumn had been lost on
the rocks of Bermuda. This circumstance, with
the Florida pirates, the heretic French and his
Spanish love of barbaric gold, fired his zeal.

The General rushed home to Spain for new
powers. Early in 1565 he stood again before
Philip petition in hand. Besides his present dig-

nities he would be Adelantado of Florida. Florida in Spanish eyes extended not only to St Mary's or the Bay of Chesapeake, but even to Newfoundland, so as to embrace the whole northern continent west of the line of demarcation. Philip had heard not only of Laudonnière and the French Huguenots the last year, but was informed of Ribault's new reinforcing expedition from Dieppe. He at once not only granted the General's request, but enlarged his powers from time to time as additional news came in of the French. Don Pedro became indeed a royal favourite. He was now a veteran of forty-seven, who had done Philip and his father personal service. He had cruised against blockaders and corsairs in early youth, had convoyed richly-laden plate fleets from the Indies; had turned the scale of victory at StQuintin in 1557 by suddenly throwing Spanish troops into Flanders greatly to the advantage of Philip; was the commanding general of the armada in which the king returned in 1559 from Flanders to Spain; had been made in 1560 captain-general

d

of the convoy or protecting fleets between Spain
and the West Indies, in which there was much
active business in guarding Spanish commerce
from corsairs. In spoiling these spoilers the
general amassed much wealth, and was acknowledged the protector of the islands and their commerce. In 1561 he had fallen into some difficulty which caused his arrest by the Council of
the Indies, but the king came to his rescue, restored his appointments, and promoted him in
1562 and 1563, and still more, as we have seen,
in 1564. In 1565 Philip gave him almost un-
limited power over Florida, with directions to
conquer, colonize, Christianize, explore and
survey, and all these too at his own expense.
Such is the fascination of royal grants. He was
given three years to perform these wonders, in
which so many others had failed. He was to
survey the coasts up to Chesapeake Bay, explore inlets and find out the hidden straits to
Cathay. Thus armed and instructed this Spanish pioneer of Virginia history and geography
returned to his native Asturias, raised an army,

manned and fitted out a fleet with many soldiers
and sailors, and 500 negro slaves. He em-
barked at Cadiz with eleven ships on the 29th
of June 1565, a fortnight after Ribault with
his seven ships had left Portsmouth. From
Porto Rico the Adelantado, in his hot haste to
forestall the French, took a new route north of
StDomingo, through the Lucayan islands and
the Bahamas, to the coast of Florida at the River
of StJohn, on the 28th of August, the day after
the arrival of the French a few miles north. Here
Menendez entered the inlet, landed his five hundred African negro slaves, founded a town, the
first in what is now the United States, and named
it StAugustine, because he made his land-fall
on the saint's-day of the great African bishop.
Thus StAugustine became the patron saint of
this first town in the United States. Here
slavery struck root, and here the Spanish Pa-
pist and the French Huguenot, brought out of
civilized and Christianized Europe were set down
blindfolded on the wild and inhospitable shores of
Florida, like two game-cocks, to fight out their

religious and implacable hatred. It was here that these 'children of the sun' showed the red men of the American forests that they too were human and mortal. Here, a few days later, the Spaniards began that merciless cut-throat religious butchery of Huguenots, to the astonishment of the savages of the primeval forests of America which finds a parallel on the pages of history only in the lesson which it taught in refined Paris just seven years later on StBartholomew's day.

All the world knows how the swift vengeance of Pedro Menendez de Avilés descended upon the unfortunate colonists of Laudonnière and Ribault and destroyed them, with very few exceptions, in September 1565. On the other hand, every one has heard how the Spaniards, almost all except the absent leader, expiated their murderous cruelty in April 1568, under the retributive justice of De Gourgues. The Spanish settlers of Florida were thus as completely exterminated by the French as the French three years before had been exterminated by the Spaniards.

After this till 1574, the Spaniards maintained possession of Florida, as far north as the Chesapeake Bay, under Menendez, who had been appointed at first Adelantado of Florida, and subsequently also Governor of Cuba. He caused an elaborate and official survey of the whole coast to be made and recorded, both in writing and in charts. Barcia tells the whole interesting story, but the charts seem to have been lost, though the description, or parts of it, remains. Menendez returned to Spain and died in 1574, just as he had been invested with the command of an 'invincible' armada of three hundred ships, and twenty thousand men to act against England and Flanders. All his North American acquisitions and surveys seem to have at once fallen into neglect. Not a Spanish town had been founded north of St Augustine. His Spanish missionaries sent among the Indians had gained no solid foot hold. Spain however still claimed possession, on paper, of the whole coast up to Newfoundland, though she could not boast of a single place of actual occupation.

England at this time began to see the coast clear

for the spread of her protestant principles in America, and for her occupation of some of those vast countries she now professed to have been the first to discover by the Cabots. No friendly power any longer stood in her way. Her relations with Spain had settled into patriotic hatred and open war. The voyages of Hawkins and Drake into the West Indies had revealed to Englishmen the enormous wealth of the Spanish trade thither, as well as the weakness of the Spanish Government in those plundered papal possessions. Frobisher had matured his plans, secured his grant, and in 1576 made his first voyage to find the north west passage. The same year the half-brother of Raleigh, Sir Humphrey Gilbert, published his 'discourse for a discouerie of a new passage to Catai,' with a map showing the coast of North America, and the passage to China. This was the result of years of study, and though the elaborate work was written out hastily at last, we know that while others were advocating the north east passage, Sir Humphrey always persisted in the north

western. Frobisher's expedition is said to have
been an outgrowth of Gilbert's efforts and pe-
titions. These projects were long in hand, but
Gilbert, in June 1578, obtained his famous
patent from Elizabeth for two hundred leagues
of any American coast not occupied by a Christian
prince. This grant was limited to six years,
to expire the eleventh of June 1584 in case no
settlement was made or colony founded. The
story of Gilbert's efforts, expenditures of himself and friends, his unparalleled misfortunes
and death, need not be retold here. Part of his
rights and privileges fell to his half-brother
Walter Raleigh who had participated somewhat in the enterprise. After Gilbert's death
and before the expiration of the patent, Raleigh
succeeded in obtaining from Elizabeth another
patent, with similar rights, privileges, and limi-
tations, dated the 25th of March 1584, leaving
the whole unoccupied coast open to his selection.
On the 27th of April, only a month later, he de-
spatched two barks under the command of Captains Amadas and Barlow, to reconnoitre the

coast, as Ribault had done, for a suitable place
to plant a colony, somewhere between Florida
and Newfoundland. This patent also, like Gilbert's, in case of negligence or non-success, was
limited to six years.   But it required the confirmation of Parliament.   Though there were
many rival interests, some of which had perhaps
to be conciliated, the patent was confirmed.

It ought perhaps to be mentioned here that
five of Gilbert's six years having already expired
without his obtaining success or possession, several others, anticipating a forfeiture of the patent, began agitation for rival patents in 1583.
Carleil, Walsingham, Sidney, Peckham, Raleigh, and perhaps others were eager in the
strife. Most of the papers are given in Hakluyt's
1589 edition.   The 'Golden Hinde' returned
in September 1583 with the news of the utter
failure of the expedition and the death of Sir
Humphrey. Raleigh succeeded in obtaining the
royal grant, and then all the rest joined him in
getting the patent confirmed by Parliament.

Raleigh was now thirty-three, a man of position, of large heart and large income, a popular courtier high in royal favor, a man of foreign travel, great experience and extensive acquirements. He had served under Coligni with his protestant friends in France; subsequently served under William of Orange in Flanders; had served his Queen in Ireland; under Gilbert's patent, contemplated a voyage to Newfound_ land in 1578; and in 1583 was ready to embark himself again, but by some happy accident did not go, though he fitted out and sent a large ship at his own cost bearing his own name, which ship however put back on account of the outbreak of some contagion. Fully alive to the wants, plans, and desires of the Huguenots, he had not only informed himself of their Florida schemes, but had promoted the publication of their history, and secured the interest and active co-operation of the most important survivor of them all, Jaques LeMoyne, the painter, who having escaped landed destitute in Wales, and subsequently entered the service of Raleigh who had him safely lodged in the Blackfriars. He had also,

e

how or when precisely is not known, secured the
active aid and facile pen of the geographical
Richard Hakluyt, who wrote for him, as no man
else could write, in 1584, a treatise on Western
Planting, a work intended probably to prime
the ministry and the Parliament, to enable Raleigh first to secure the confirmation of his patent, and afterwards the co-operation and active
interest of the nobility and gentry in his enterprise. This important hitherto unpublished volume of sixty-three large folio pages in the handwriting of Hakluyt, after having probably served
its purpose and lain dormant for nearly three centuries, was bought at Earl Mountnorris's sale
at Arley Castle in December 1852, by Mr Henry
Stevens of Vermont, who, as he himself informs
us, after partly copying it, and endeavouring in
vain to place it in some public or private library
in England or the United States, threw it into
auction, where it was sold by Messrs Puttick
and Simpson in May 1854, for £44, as lot 474,
Sir Thomas Phillipps being the purchaser. The
manuscript still adorns the Phillipps library at

Cheltenham. In 1868 a copy of this most suggestive volume was obtained by the late Dr Leonard Woods for the Maine Historical Society, and has since been edited with valuable notes by Mr Charles Deane of Cambridge and with an Introduction by Dr Woods. It appeared in 1877 as the second volume of the second series of the Society's Collections.

This Treatise of Hakluyt under Raleigh's inspiration may be regarded as the harbinger of Virginia history. Though intended for a special purpose, it is of the highest importance in developing the history of English maritime policy at that time, and defining the growth of the English arguments, advantages and reasons for western planting. The book is full of personal hints, and is immensely suggestive, showing us more than anything else the master hand of Master Hakluyt in moulding England's ' sea policie ' and colonial navigation. No mere geographical study by Hakluyt could alone have produced this remarkable volume. It is the combination of many materials, and the result of compromising divers interests. Hakluyt had already, though still a young man under thirty, entered deeply into the study of commercial geography, and had in 1582 published his *Divers Voyages* dedicated to his friend Sir Philip Sidney, son-in-law to the chief Secretary Walsingham. In the Spring of 1583 the Secretary sent Hakluyt down to Bristol with a letter to the principal merchants there to enlist their co-operation in a project of discovery and planting in America somewhere between the possessions of the French in Canada and the Spaniards in Florida, which his son-in-law Master Christopher Carleil was developing under the auspices of the Muscovie Company, and for which they were about to ask the Queen for a patent independent of Sir Humphrey Gilbert's.

In the summer of 1583 Hakluyt thought to go to Newfoundland with Gilbert's expedition, according to the letter of Parmenius, but fortunately did not go. But in the autumn of the same year Walsingham sent him to Paris nominally as chaplain to the English Ambassador at the

French court, Sir Edward Stafford, but really to pursue his geographical investigations into the west and learn what the French and Spanish were doing in these remote regions, and what were their particular claims, resources and trade.

Before his departure for Paris, the 'Golden Hinde' had returned to Falmouth with the heavy news of the fate of Gilbert and the consequent certain forfeiture of his patent, notwithstanding it had still some nine months to run. Though Sir Humphrey had taken formal possession of Newfoundland, as no colony was left there, his rights and privileges would lapse as a matter of course.

Western planting now became the talk and fashion. Many projects were hatching for new patents. Raleigh alone succeeded. Hakluyt's position and circumstances in Paris seem made for the occasion, and he soon found all these western eggs put into his basket. The materials of the several previous writers and of the rival claimants were all apparently thrust upon him. He thus became in 1583-4, though perhaps un-

consciously, the mouthpiece of a snug family party
all playing into the hands of Raleigh.   There
were Walsingham, and Sidney, and Carleil,
and Leicester, all connected with each other and
with Raleigh.   Then there were the papers of
Sir George Peckham, Edward Hayes, Richard
Clarke master of the Delight, and Steven Parmenius, rich alike in hints and facts.   The interests of these distinguished persons were by
family ties or other influence suddenly merged
into a single patent and that Raleigh's.   The
papers mostly passed through Raleigh's hands
into Hakluyt's, who acknowledges himself indebted to him for his chiefest light.

Raleigh, besides being the half-brother and
representative of Sir Humphrey Gilbert, held
also a large share in that venture.   Gilbert's real
aim, policy and plan, in this last year of his patent,
to prospect for a suitable place in which to take
possession and found a colony, was to begin at
the south and work northward as the French
had done, but his previous failures since 1578,
the inevitable impediments and delays, the ad-

vanced season of this his last year 1583, and
the necessity of making a final strike for success,
in behalf of himself and his assignees, compelled
him at the last hour to go direct to Newfoundland, take possession, and then, if thought best,
work southward. He was however unquestionably influenced or professed to be by rumours of
metals or gold mines in Newfoundland. This
northern passage was his fatal mistake. Had
he taken a middle or southern course say between 37° and 42° he might perhaps have succeeded.

Under these circumstances Hakluyt's Discourse of Western Planting was written, and
may be considered as a digest of many plans
without much originality and a consolidation of
many interests. Hakluyt and Raleigh were at
Oxford together, but we find no particular evidence of their intimacy before the Spring of
1584, when Hakluyt had returned to London
from Paris with his Discourse, or perhaps it was
partly written in England. It is pretty certain that
it was not shown to the Queen before the date

of the Patent, the 25th of March, as Hakluyt
speaks of her seeing it in the summer. It was
probably intended principally for the promotion
of the interests of the Patent in Parliament.

At all events with his investigations in France
Hakluyt's Discourse became thoroughly English
in its tone and tenor, and from this time he labored zealously in the interests of Raleigh. A
main point of inquiry in Paris was to avail himself of the many opportunities at the Spanish and
Portuguese embassies, and with the French merchants and sailors of Paris, Rouen, Havre and
Dieppe, to pick up the particulars of the West
India trade of the Spaniards, and the nature of
the French dealings in Cape Breton and Canada.
This led him to set forth the advantages of direct
English western trade independent of France
and Spain, and of French and Spanish routes.

The fisheries of Newfoundland and the Banks
were extensive, and by repeated treaties neutral,
but gave no exclusive rights on the adjoining terri-
tory to any one of the fishing nations; though in
all cases the English by common consent exercised

leadership in the Newfoundland harbors among the fishing ships, of which there were now some six or eight hundred a year, notwithstanding the English still fished also at Iceland.

It was necessary however in the interests of England for Hakluyt in this Discourse to revive and substantiate the English rights in America by putting forward the prior discovery by the Cabots in 1497-1498. Though he presents this direct claim modestly, yet like Sir Humphrey Gilbert he founds it upon insufficient evidence. In a loose manner he speaks of Cabot and not the Cabots, and attributes to Sebastian the son what properly belongs to John the father. He reposes full confidence in the loose and gossiping statements of Peter Martyr that Sebastian Cabot, a quarter of a century after the discovery, told him that at the time, 1497 or 98, he had explored the coast to the latitude of Gibraltar, that is to Chesapeake Bay and the longitude of Cuba or the city of Cincinnati, a thing not probable, in as much as the active old pilot mayor was never able to declare, down to the time of Gomez, that he had

f

been on that coast before. It would have been foolish in him to fit out in 1524 Gomez to ' discover' what the pilot mayor had already explored in 1497.

Hakluyt's arguments and historical statements in this Discourse of 1584 to the present time have always been presented by English diplomatists with confidence, especially against the French. Yet the French continued to maintain their occupation of Cape Breton, the Gulf of St Lawrence and Canada, which together they called New France. It is now however made apparent from contemporary historical documents that have recently been brought to light from the archives of Spain and Venice that John Cabot, accompanied by his son Sebastian, then a youth of some nineteen or twenty years, in 1497 took possession of Cape Breton in the names of Venice and England conjointly, and raised the flags of St Mark and St George. There is not yet any trustworthy evidence that they went south of Cape Breton either in that or the voyage of 1498.

Hakluyt in his Divers Voyages in 1582 did

not venture to make this Cabot claim so strong as in this Discourse. In his dedication to Sir Philip Sidney he quaintly says that he 'put downe the title which we haue to this part of America which is from Florida to 67 degrees northwarde by the letters patentes graunted to Iohn Cabote and his three sonnes,' simply meaning that he had printed the first patent of 5th May 1496. In his title page he speaks of the Discoverie of America, 'made first of all by our Englishmen and afterwards by the Frenchmen and Bretons.' He does not question the rights and privileges of Frenchmen to the Gulf of St Lawrence and Canada, because they were in the occupation of a Christian prince.

This Discourse of Western Planting therefore, and the voyage of Amadas and Barlow, in 1584, at the instigation and expense of Raleigh, based on a thorough knowledge of the Huguenot and Spanish expeditions to Florida in 1562-1568, are all parts of Virginia history, and therefore are preliminary to Hariot's Report. It should be borne in mind that these terms Florida and Virginia as used by the Spaniards, French, and English, included the whole country from the point of Florida through the Carolinas and Virginia to the Chesapeake Bay, or perhaps even to Bacalaos.

Raleigh's patent, in which all interests were thus consolidated, came before Parliament in the Autumn of 1584 well fortified in its historical and geographical bearings by Hakluyt's learned Discourse. In the House of Commons the matter was adroitly referred to a Commitee of which Walsingham and Sir Philip Sidney, Sir Christopher Hatton and Sir Francis Drake were members. The bill having passed the House was sent up to the Lords, and there read the first time on Sunday the 19th of December 1584, as appears by the following entry in the Lords' Journal, volume ii, page 76. 'Hodie allatæ sicut a Domo Communi 4 Billæ; *Prima*, For the Confirmation of the Queen's Majesty's Letters Patents, granted to Walter Raughlieghe, Esquire, touching the Discovery and Inhabiting of certain Foreign Lands and Countries, quæ 1ᵃ *vice* lecta est.' It does not appear precisely at what date the Bill received the Queen's signature, but probably as early as Christmas or New Year.

Having now early in 1585 secured the Confirmation of this much coveted patent which liberally permitted him in the name and under the ægis of England to plant a 'colonie' and found an English empire in the New World at his own expense of money, men, and enterprise; having pocketed the geographical results and valuable experience of the French in Florida and Canada; having vainly attempted a visit to Newfoundland in 1578, and having succeeded to the rights and privileges of his noble half-brother Sir Humphrey Gilbert; having received by the return in September of his two reconnoitring barks favorable reports as to the properest place to begin his Western Planting in Wingandacoa; and being thoroughly supported by the good wishes and hearty co-operation of the Queen and many of her prominent and influential subjects, Raleigh rose superior to all jealousies and opposition.

This lasted as usual just so long as he was successful and no longer. But he was blessed in his
household, or at his table, or in his confidence,
with four sterling adherents who stuck to him
through thick and thin, through prosperity and adversity. These were Richard Hakluyt, Jaques
Le Moyne, John White and Thomas Hariot.
When Wingandacoa makes up her jewels she
will not forget these Four, whom it is just to
call Raleigh's Magi.

With marvellous energy, enterprise, and skill
Raleigh collected and fitted out in an incredibly
short time a fleet of seven ships well stocked and
well manned to transport his ' first colonie ' into
the wilds of America. It was under the command of his valiant cousin, Admiral Sir Richard Grenville, and sailed from Plymouth on the
19th of May 1585. Never before did a finer
fleet leave the shores of England, and never since
was one more honestly or hopefully dispatched.
There were the ' Tyger ' and the ' Roe Buck '
of 140 tons each, the ' Lyon' of 100 tons, the
' Elizabeth' of 50 tons, the ' Dorothea,' a small

bark, and two pinnaces, hardly big enough to bear distinct names, yet small enough to cross dangerous bars and enter unknown bays and rivers. In this splendid outfit were nearly two hundred souls, among whom were Master Ralfe Lane as governor of the colony, Thomas Candish or Cavendish afterwards the circumnavigator, Captain Philip Amadas of the Council, John White the painter as delineator and draughtsman, Master Thomas Hariot the mathematician as historiographer, surveyor and scientific discoverer or explorer, and many others whose names are preserved in Hakluyt.

The fleet had a prosperous voyage by the then usual route of the West Indies and fell in with the main of Florida on the 20th of June, made and named Cape Fear on the 23d, and a first landing the next day, and on the 26th came to Wococa where Amadas and Barlow had been the year before. They disembarked and at first mistook the country for Paradise. July was spent in surveying and exploring the country, making the acquaintance of the natives, chiefly by means

of two Indians that had been taken to England
and brought back able to speak English. On
the 5th of August Master John Arundel, captain of one of the vessels, was sent back to England, and on the 25th of August Admiral Grenville, after a sojourn of two months in Virginia,
took his leave and returned, arriving at Plymouth
on the 18th of October. There were left in Virginia as Raleigh's ' First Colonie,' one hundred
and nine men. They remained there one whole
year and then, discontented, returned to England
in July 1586 in Sir Francis Drake's fleet coming
home victorious from the West Indies.

One of these 109 men was Thomas Hariot
the Author of the Report of Virginia. Another
was John White the painter. To these two
earnest and true men we owe, as has been said,
nearly all we know of 'Ould Virginia.' Their
story is briefly told by Hakluyt.

Sir Francis Drake in the true spirit of friendship went out of his way to make this call on the
Colony of his friend Raleigh. He found them
anything but contented and prosperous. They

had long been expecting supplies and reinforce-
ments from home, which not arriving, on the departure of Drake's fleet becoming dejected and
homesick, they petitioned the Governor for permission to return.   Immediately after their departure a ship arrived from Raleigh, and fourteen days later Sir Richard Grenville himself
returned with his fleet of three ships, new planters and stores of supplies, only to find the
Colony deserted and no tidings to be had.
Leaving twenty men to hold possession the Admiral made his way back to England.

It has already been stated how and under what
circumstances the epitome of the labours and surveys of Hariot came to be printed, but it may be
well to show how it came to be united with John
White's drawings and republished a year or two
later as the first part of De Bry's celebrated collections of voyages.   Hakluyt returned to Paris
at the end of 1584 and remained there, perhaps
with an occasional visit to London, till 1588, always working in the interests of Raleigh.   In
April 1585, a month before the departure of the

Virginia fleet, he wrote to Walsingham that he 'was careful to advertise Sir Walter Raleigh from tyme to tyme and send him discourses both in print and in written hand concerning his voyage.'

Réné Goulaine de Laudonnière's Journal had fallen into Hakluyt's hand, and he induced his friend Basanier the mathematician to edit and publish it. This was done and the work was dedicated to Raleigh and probably paid for by him. Le Moyne the painter and mathematician who had accompanied the expedition, one of the few who escaped into the woods and swamps with Laudonnière the dreadful morning of the massacre, was named by Basanier. He also mentions a lad named De Bry who was lucky enough to find his way out of the clutches of the Spanish butchers into the hands of the more merciful American Savages. This young man was found by De Gourgues nearly three years later among the Indians that joined him in his mission of retribution against the Spaniards, and was restored to his friends well instructed in the ways, manners and customs of the Florida Aborigines.

This journal of Laudonnière carefully edited by Basanier was completed in time to be published in Paris in 1586, in French, in octavo. It was dedicated to Sir Walter Raleigh. Hakluyt translated it into English, and printed it in small quarto in London the next year and it reappeared again in his folio voyages of 1589. The French edition fell under the eye of Theodore De Bry the afterwards celebrated engraver of Frankfort, formerly of Liège. Whether or not this engraver was a relative of young De Bry of Florida is not known, but we are told that he soon sought out Le Moyne whom he found in Raleigh's service living in the Blackfriars in London, acting as painter, engraver on wood, a teacher and art publisher or bookseller.

De Bry first came to London in 1587 to see Le Moyne and arrange with him about illustrating Laudonnière's Journal with the artist's maps and paintings, and remained here some time, but did not succeed in obtaining what he wanted, probably because Le Moyne was meditating a similar work of his own, and being still at-

tached to the household of Raleigh was not free
to negotiate for that peculiar local and special
information which he had already placed at Raleigh's disposal for his colony planted a little
north of the French settlement in Florida, then
supposed to be in successful operation, but of
which nothing had yet been published to give
either the world at large or the Spaniards in the
peninsula a premature clue to his enterprise.

There is still preserved a good memorial of De
Bry's visit to London in the celebrated funeral
pageant at the obsequies of Sir Philip Sidney in
the month of February 1587, drawn and invented
by T. Lant and engraved on copper by Theodore de Bry in the city of London, 1587.   A
complete copy is in the British Museum, and
another is said to be at the old family seat of the
Sidneys at Penshurst in Kent, now Lord de
L'Isle's; while a third copy not quite perfect
adorns the famous London collection of Mr Gard-
ner of St John's Wood Park.

Le Moyne died in 1588, and De Bry soon after
came to London a second time and succeeded in

purchasing of the widow of Le Moyne a portion of the artist's drawings or paintings together with his version of the French Florida Expeditions. While here this time De Bry fell in with Richard Hakluyt, who had returned from Paris in November 1588, escorting Lady Sheffield.

Hakluyt at the end of this year, or the beginning of 1589, was engaged in seeing through the press his first folio collection of the voyages of the English, finished, according to the date in the preface, the 17th of November, though entered at Stationers' Hall on the strength of a note from Walsingham the first of September previous. Hakluyt with his mind full of voyages and travels was abundantly competent to appreciate De Bry's project of publishing a luxurious edition of Laudonnière's Florida illustrated with the exquisite drawings of Le Moyne. Ever ready to make a good thing better, Hakluyt suggested the addition of Le Moyne's and other Florida papers; and introduced De Bry to John White, Governor of Virginia, then in London.

White, an English painter of eminence and

merit, was as an artist to Virginia what Le Moyne
his master had been to Florida. Le Moyne had
twenty years before mapped and pictured everything in Florida from the River of May to Cape
Fear, and White had done the same for Raleigh's
Colony in Virginia (now North Carolina) from
Cape Fear to the Chesapeake Bay. Le Moyne
had spent a year with Laudonnière at Fort Caro-
line in 1564-65, and White had been a whole year
in and about Roanoke and the wilderness of
Virginia in 1585-86 as the right hand man of
Hariot.

Together Hariot and White surveyed, mapped, pictured and described the country, the Indians, men and women; the animals, birds, fishes,
trees, plants, fruits and vegetables. Hariot's Report or epitome of his Chronicle, reproduced by
the Hercules Club, was privately printed in
February 1589. A volume containing seventy-
six of White's original drawings in water colours
is now preserved in the Grenville library in the
British Museum, purchased by the Trustees in
March 1866 of Mr Henry Stevens at the in-

stigation of Mr Panizzi, and placed there as an appropriate pendant to the world-renowned Grenville De Bry. This is the very volume that White painted for Raleigh, and which served De Bry for his Virginia. Only 23 out of the 76 drawings were engraved, the rest never yet having been published. Thus Hariot's text and map with White's drawings are necessary complements to each other and should be mentioned together.

Knowing all these men and taking an active part in all these important events, Hakluyt acted wisely in inducing De Bry to modify his plan of a separate publication and make a Collection of illustrated Voyages. He suggested first that the separate work of Florida should be suspended, and enlarged with Le Moyne's papers, outside of Laudonnière. Then reprint, as a basis of the Collection, Hariot's privately printed Report on Virginia just coming out in February 1589, and illustrate it with the map and White's drawings. Hakluyt engaged to write descriptions of the plates, and his geographical touches are easily recognizable in the maps of both Virginia and Florida.

In this way De Bry was induced to make Hariot's Virginia the First Part of his celebrated PEREGRINATIONS, with a dedication to Sir Walter Raleigh. Florida then became the Second Part. The first was illustrated from the portfolio of John White, and the second from that of Jaques Le Moyne. Both parts are therefore perfectly authentic and trustworthy. Thus the famous Collections of De Bry may be said to be of English origin, for to Raleigh and his magi De Bry owed everything in the start of his great work. Being thus supplied and instructed, De Bry returned to Frankfort, and with incredible energy and enterprise, engraved, printed, and issued his VIRGINIA in four languages, English, French, Latin and German, in 1590, and his Florida in Latin and German, in 1591. The bibliographical history of these books; the intimacy and dependence of the several persons engaged; and the geographical development of Florida-Virginia are all so intertwined and blended, that the whole seems to lead up to Thomas Hariot, the clearing up of whose biography thus becomes an appropriate labor of the Hercules Club.

Little more remains to be said of Raleigh's Magi who have been thus shown to be hand and glove in working out these interesting episodes of French and English colonial history. To Hakluyt, Le Moyne, White, De Bry and Hariot, Raleigh owes an undivided and indivisible debt of gratitude for the prominent niche which he achieved in the world's history, especially in that of England and America ; while to Raleigh's liberal heart and boundless enterprise must be ascribed a generous share of the reputation achieved by his Magi in both hemispheres.

Of Hakluyt and De Bry little more need be said here. They both hewed out their own fortunes and recorded them on the pages of history, the one with his pen, the other with his graver. If at times ill informed bibliographers who have got beyond their depth fail to discern its merits,

h

and endeavour to deny or depreciate De Bry's Collection, charging it with a want of authenticity and historic truth, it is hoped that enough has been said here to vindicate at least the first two parts, Virginia and Florida. The remaining parts, it is believed, can be shown to be of equal authority.

Whoever compares the original drawings of Le Moyne and White with the engravings of De Bry, as one may now do in the British Museum, must be convinced that, beautiful as De Bry's work is, it seems tame in the presence of the original water-colour drawings. There is no exaggeration in the engravings.

Le Moyne's name has not found its way into modern dictionaries of art or biography, but he was manifestly an artist of great merit and a man of good position. In addition to what is given above it may be added that a considerable number of his works is still in existence, and it is hoped will hereafter be duly appreciated. In the print-room of the British Museum are two of his drawings, highly finished in water-colours, being unquestionably the originals of plates eight and forty-one of De Bry's Florida. They are about double the size of the engravings. They came in with the Sloane Collection.

There is also in the Manuscript Department of the British Museum a volume of original drawings relating chiefly to Florida and Virginia (Sloane N° 5270) manifestly a mixture of Le Moyne's and White's sketches. They are very valuable. There is also in the Museum library a printed and manuscript book by Le Moyne, which speaks for itself and tells its own interesting story. It is in small oblong quarto and is entitled ' ☞ La/ Clef des Champs,/ pour trouuer plusieurs Ani-/maux, tant Bestes qu'Oy-/seaux, auec/ plusieurs Fleurs & Fruitz./ Anno. 1586./ ¶ Imprimé aux Blackfriers, pour Jaques/ le Moyne, dit de Morgues Paintre/'. The book consists of fifty leaves, of which two are preliminary containing the title and on the reverse and third page a neat dedication in French ' A Ma-dame Ma-dame/ De Sidney.'/ Signed ' Vostre tres-affectionné,/ IAQVES LE MOINE dit

de/ MORGVES Paintre.'/   This dedication is
dated 'Londres/ ce xxvi. de Mars.'/   On the
reverse of the second leaf, also in French, is
'¶ A Elle Mesme,/ Sonet' with the initials
I.L.M.

Then follow forty-eight leaves with two wood-
cuts coloured by hand on the recto of each leaf,
reverse blank. These ninety-six cuts sum up
twenty-four each of beasts, birds, fruits and flowers, with names printed under each in English,
French, German and Latin. Although the book
is dated the 26th of March 1586, it was not
entered at Stationers' Hall until the 31st of July
1587. It there stands under the name of James
Le Moyne alias Morgan. Madame Sidney is
given as Mary Sidney.   She was sister of Sir
Philip, countess of Pembroke, 'Sidney's sister,
Pembroke's mother.' There is no allusion to Sir
Philip in the dedication, and therefore we may
infer that it was penned before the battle of Zut-
phen. Both the dedication and the sonnet show
the artist's intimacy and friendship with that distinguished family.

There are two copies of this exceedingly rare book in the British Museum, both slightly imperfect, but will together make a complete one, but the more interesting copy is that in $727 \frac{c}{2} 31$, in the Sloane Collection. It has bound up with it thirty-seven leaves on which are beautifully drawn and painted flowers, fruits, birds &c. There can be little doubt that these are Le Moyne's own paintings. It is curious to find that all these scattered works in the different departments came in with the Sloane Collection which formed the nucleus of the British Museum. It is to be hoped that other samples of Le Moyne's art may be found or identified, and that all of them may be brought together or be described as the ' Le Moyne Collection.' How Sir Hans Sloane became possessed of them does not yet appear.

Capt. John White's name in the annals of English art is destined to rank high, though it has hitherto failed to be recorded in the art histories and dictionaries. Yet his seventy-six original paintings in water-colours done probably in Virginia in 1585-1586 while he was there with Hariot as the official draughtsman or painter of Raleigh's ' First Colonie ' entitle him to prominence among English artists in Elizabeth's reign. There are some other works of his in the Manuscript department mingled with those of his friend and master Le Moyne.

As Raleigh's friend and agent White's name deserves honorable mention in the history of ' Ould Virginia.' He was an original adventurer in the ' First Colonie ' and was one of the hundred and nine who spent a whole year at and about Roanoke and returned with Drake in 1586. He went again to Virginia in April 1587 as Governor of Raleigh's ' Second Colonie,' consisting of one hundred and fifty persons in three ships, being the fourth expedition. Raleigh appointed to him twelve assistants ' to whome he gave a Charter, and incorporated them by the name of Governour and Assistants of the Citie of Raleigh in Virginia,' intended to be founded on the Chesapeake Bay. It never became more than a ' paper city.'

This Second Colony landed at Roanoke the 20th of July, but finding themselves disappointed and defeated in all points, the colonists joined in urging the Governor to return to England for supplies and instructions. He reluctantly departed the 27th of August from Roanoke, leaving there his daughter, who was the mother of the first child of English parents born in English North America, Virginia Dare. He intended immediately to return to Virginia with relief, but the embarrassments of Raleigh, the stirring times, and the 'Spanish Armada' defeated Sir Walter and frustrated all his plans.

On the 20th of November 1587 Governor White having reached home apprised Raleigh of the circumstances and requirements of the Colony. Sir Walter at once ' appointed a pinnesse to be sent thither with all such necessaries as he vnderſtood they stood in neede of,' and also ' wrote his letters vnto them, wherein among other matters he comforted them with promise, that with all conuenient speede he would prepare a good supply of shipping and men with sufficience

of all thinges needefull, which he intended, God
willing, should be with them the Sommer following.' This promised fleet was got ready in
the harbor of Bideford under the personal care
and supervision of Sir Richard Grenville, and
waited only for a fair wind to put to sea. Then
came news of the proposed invasion of England
by Philip King of Spain with his 'invincible
armada,' so wide spread and alarming that it
was deemed prudent by the Government to stay
all ships fit for war in any ports of England
to be in readiness for service at home ; and even
Sir Richard Grenville was commanded not to
leave Cornwall.

Governor White however having left about
one hundred and twenty men, women and children in Virginia, among whom were his own
daughter and granddaughter, left no stone un-
turned for their relief. He labored so earnestly
and successfully that he obtained two small 'pin-
neses ' named the 'Brave' and the ' Roe,' one of
thirty and the other of twenty-five tons, 'wherein
fifteen planters and all their provision, with cer-

tain reliefe for those that wintered in the Countrie was to be transported.'

The ' Brave' and the ' Roe' with this slender
equipment passed the bar of Bideford the 22nd
of April, just six months after the return of the
Governor, a small fleet with small hope. Had
it been larger its going forth would not have been
permitted. The Governor remained behind, think-
ing he could serve the Colony better in England.
But the sailors of the little ' Brave' and ' Roe' had
caught the fighting mania before they sailed,
and instead of going with all speed to the relief of
Virginia, scoured the seas for rich prizes, and like
two little fighting cocks let loose attacked every
sail they caught sight of, friend or foe. The
natural consequence was that before they reached
Madeira (they took the southern course for the
sake of plunder) they had been several times
thoroughly whipped, and ' all thinges spilled '
in their fights.   ' By this occasion, God iustly
punishing the theeuerie of our euil disposed ma-
riners, we were of force constrained to break of
our voyage intended for the reliefe of our Colony

i

left the yere before in Virginia, and the same
night to set our course for England.' In a month
from their departure they recrossed the bar of
Bideford, their voyage having been a disgrace-
ful failure, yet the doings of these two miniature
corsairs are recorded in Hakluyt manifestly
only as specimens of English pluck, a British
quality always admired, however much misdi-
rected.   Meanwhile no tidings of the ' Second
colonie ' and worse still, no tidings or help had
the Second Colony received all this long time
from England.   And even to this day the echo is
'no tidings' and no help from home. This then
may be called the first and great human sacrifice
that savage America required of civilized England before yielding to her inevitable destiny.

And so it was that Virginia and the Armada
Year shook the fortunes of Raleigh and compelled him to assign a portion of his Patent
and privileges under it to divers gentlemen
and merchants of London.   This document, in
which are included and protected the charter
rights of White and others in the ' City of

Raleigh,' bears date the 7th of March 1589. Matters being thus settled, with more capital and new life a 'Fifth Expedition' was fitted out in 1590 in which Governor White went out to carry aid, and to reinforce his long neglected colony of 1587. Not one survivor was found, and White returned the same year in every way unsuccessful. He soon after retired to Raleigh's estates in Ireland, and the last heard of him is a long letter to his friend Hakluyt 'from my house at Newtowne in Kylmore the 4th of February 1593.'

Raleigh's Patent, like that of Gilbert, would have expired by the limitation of six years on the 24th of March 1590 if he had not succeeded in leading out a colony and taking possession. His first colony of 1585 was voluntarily abandoned, but not his discoveries. His second colony of 1587 was surrounded with so much obscurity that though in fact he maintained no real and permanent settlement, yet it was never denied that he lawfully took possession and inhabited Virginia within the six years and also

for a time in the seventh year, and therefore
was entitled to privileges extending two hundred leagues from Roanoke. As long as Elizabeth lived no one disputed Raleigh's privileges
under his patent, though partly assigned, but
none of the Assignees cared to adventure further.
The patent had become practically a dead letter.

As late however as 1603 the compliment was
paid Raleigh of asking his permission to make a
voyage to North Virginia. As no English plantation between the Spanish and the French possessions in North America at the time of the ac-
cession of James was maintained the patent was
allowed nominally to remain in force. But no
one claimed any rights under it. It has been
stated by several recent historians that the at-
tainder of Raleigh took away his patent privileges, but evidence of this is not forthcoming.
It is manifest that James the First, who had
little regard for his own or others' royal grants
or chartered rights in America, considered the
coast clear and as open to his own royal bounty
as it had been long before to Pope Alexander

the Sixth. It was easier and safer to obtain new charters than to revive any questionable old ones.

But to all intents and purposes the interesting history of Virginia begins with Raleigh. Whence he drew his inspiration, how he profited by the experience of others, how he patronized his Magi and bound them to himself with cords of friendship and liberality; how by his very blunders and misfortunes he transmitted to posterity some of the most precious historical memorials found on the pages of English or American history, we have, perhaps at unnecessary length, endeavoured to show in this long essay on the brief and true Report of Thomas Hariot, his surveyor and topographer in Virginia, which must ever serve as the corner-stone of English American History, by a man who, though long neglected and half forgotten, must eventually shine as the morning star of the mathematical sciences in England, as well as that of the history of her Empire in the West.

It remains now to give some personal account

of Thomas Hariot, whose first book as the first
of the labors of the HERCULES CLUB has been
reproduced.   Every incident in the life of a
man of eminent genius and originality in any
country is a lesson to the world's posterity deserving careful record.   Hitherto dear quaint
old positive antiquarianly slippery Anthony à
Wood in his *Athenæ Oxoniensis* embodies nearly
all of our accepted notions of this great English
mathematician and philosopher.   Anthony was
indefatigable in his researches into the biography
of Hariot who was both an Cxford man and an
Oxford scholar. He happily succeeded in mousing
out a goodly number of recondite and particular
occurrences of Hariot's life.   He managed, however, to state very many of them erroneously ;
and he drew hence some important inferences,
the reverse, as it now appears, of historical
truth.   This naturally leads one to inquire into
his authorities.   Wood's account of Hariot appeared in his first edition of 1691, and has not
been improved in the two subsequent editions.
For most of his facts he appears to have been

indebted to Dr John Wallis's Algebra, first
published in 1685, though ready for the printer
in 1676 ; and for his fictions to poor old gossiping Aubrey ; while his inferences, in respect to
Hariot's deism and disbelief in the Scriptures,
are probably his own, as we find no sufficient
trace of them prior to the appearance of his
Athenæ, unless it be in Chief Justice Popham's
unjust charge at Winchester in 1603, when he
is said to have twitted Raleigh from the bench
with having been ' bedeviled ' by Hariot.   Dr
Wallis appears to have obtained part of his facts
from John Collins, who had been in his usual
indefatigable manner looking up Hariot and his
papers as early as 1649, and wrote to the doctor
of his success several letters between 1667 and
1673, which may be seen in Professor Rigaud's
Correspondence of Scientific Men of the Seventeenth Century, 2 vols, Oxford, 1841, 8°.

Since 1784, from time to time, several other
writers have partly repeated Wood's estimate
and added several new facts, as will be shown
further on.   But it has been reserved for the

Hercules Club, now just three hundred years after Hariot left the University, to bring to light new and important contemporary evidence, sufficient, it is believed, to considerably modify our general estimate of Hariot's life and character, and to raise him from the second rank of mathematicians to which Montucla coolly relegated him nearly a century ago to the pre-eminence of being one of the foremost scholars of his age, not alone of England but of the world. Had he been walled around by church bigotry like his friend and contemporary Galileo he would unquestionably by the originality and brilliancy of his observations and discoveries have rivalled, or perhaps have shared that philosopher's victories in science. At all events it is believed that the new matter is sufficient to reopen the courts of criticism and revision in which some of the decisions respecting the use of perspective glasses, the invention of the telescope, the discoveries of the spots on the sun, the satellites of Jupiter and the horns of Venus may be reconsidered and perhaps reversed. It is believed that in logical analysis, in philosophy, and in many other departments of science few in his day were his equals, while in pure mathematics none was his superior.

Thomas Hariot was born at Oxford, or as Anthony à Wood with more than his usual quaintness expresses it, ' tumbled out of his mother's womb into the lap of the Oxonian muses in 1560.' He was a ' bateler or commoner of St Mary's hall.' He ' took the degree of bachelor of arts in 1579, and in the latter end of that year did compleat it by determination in Schoolstreet.' Nothing of his boyhood, or of his family, except a few hints in his will, has come to light.

It is not known precisely at what time Hariot joined Walter Raleigh, who was only eight years his senior. From what their friend Hakluyt says of them both, their intimate friendship and mutually serviceable connection were already an old story as early as 1587. On the eighth calends of March 1587, that is on the 22d of February 1588, present reckoning, Hakluyt wrote from Paris to Raleigh in London,

k

'To you therefore I have freely desired to give
and dedicate these my labors.   For to whom
could I present these *Decades of the New World*
[of Peter Martyr] more appropriately than to
yourself, who, at the expense of nearly one hundred thousand ducats, with new fleets, are showing to us of modern times new regions, leading
forth a third colony [to Virginia], giving us
news of the unknown, and opening up for us
pathways through the inaccessible ;   and whose
every care, and thought, and effort tend towards this end, hinge upon and adhere to it ?
To whom have been present and still are present the same ideas, desires, & incentives as with
that most illustrious Charles Howard, the Second
Neptune of the Ocean, and Edward Stafford
our most prudent Ambassador at the Court of
France, in order to accomplish great deeds by
sea and land.   But since by your skill in the
art of navigation you clearly saw that the chief
glory of an insular kingdom would obtain its
greatest splendor among us by the firm support
of the mathematical sciences, you have trained

up and supported *now a long time*, with a most liberal salary, Thomas Hariot, a young man well versed in those studies, in order that you might acquire in your spare hours by his instruction a knowledge of these noble sciences ; and your own numerous Sea Captains might unite profitably theory with practice. What is to be the result shortly of this your wise and learned school, they who possess even moderate judgment can have no difficulty in guessing. This one thing I know, the one and only consideration to place before you, that first the Portuguese and afterwards the Spaniards formerly made great endeavours with no small loss, but at length succeeded through determination of mind. Hasten on then to adorn the Sparta [Virginia] you have discovered ; hasten on that ship more than Argonautic, of nearly a thousand tons burthen which you have at last built and finished with truly regal expenditure, to join with the rest of the fleet you have fitted out.'

From this extract one might perhaps reasonably infer that Hariot went directly from the

University in 1580 at the age of twenty into
Raleigh's service, or at latest in 1582 when Raleigh returned from Flanders. As our translation of this important passage is rather a free
one the old geographer's words are here added,
in his own peculiar Latin. Hakluyt in his edition of Peter Martyr's Eight Decades, printed
at Paris in 1587, 8°, writes of his young friend
Hariot in his dedication to his older friend Sir
Walter Raleigh, as follows :—

Tibi igitur has meas vigilias condonatas & confecratas effe
volui. Cui enim potius, quàm tibi has noui Orbis Decades
offerem, qui centum ferè millium ducatorũ impenfa, nouis tuis
clafsibus regiones nouas, nouam iam tertiò ducendo coloniam,
notas ex ignotis, ex inaccefsis peruias, nouifsimis hifce tẽporibus
nobis exhibes ?   Cuius omnes curæ, cogitationes, conatus, huc
fpectant, hæc verfant, in his inhærent.   Cui cum Illuftrifsimo
illo herôe, Carolo Hovvardo, altero Oceani maris Neptuno,
Edoardi Staffordij, noftri apud regem Chriftianifsimum oratoris
prudentifsimi fororio, eadem ftudia, eædem voluntates, iidem
ad res magnas terra maríque aggrediendas funt & fuerunt ani-
morum ftimuli.   Cùm vero artis nauigatoriæ peritia, præcipuum
regni infularis ornamentum, Mathematicarũ fcientiarũ admini-
culis adhibitis, fuũ apud nos fplendorẽ poffe cõfequi facilè per-
fpiceres, Thomam Hariotum, iuuenem in illis difciplinis excel-
lentẽ, honeftifsimo falario iamdiu donatum apud te aluifti, cuius
fubfidio horis fuccefsiuis nobilifsimas fcientias illas addifceres,
tuique familiares duces maritimi, quos habes non paucos, cum
praxi theoriã non fine fructu incredibili cõiungerẽt.   Ex quo

pulcherrimo & fapientifsimo inftituto tuo, quid breui euentutum
fit, qui vel mediocri iudicio volent, facilè proculdubio diuinare
poterunt. Vnum hoc fcio, vnam & vnicam rationem te inire,
qua primò Lufitani, deinde Caftellani, quod antea toties cum nõ
exigua iactura funt conati, tandem ex animorũ votis perficerũt.
Perge ergo Spartam quam nactus es ornare, perge nauem illam
plufquam Argonauticam, mille cuparum fere capacẽ, quam
fumptibus plane regiis fabricatam iam tãdem fœliciter abfoluifti,
reliquæ tuæ clafsi, quam habes egregiè inftructam, adiungere.

From this early time for nearly forty years,
till the morning of the 29th of October 1618,
when Raleigh was beheaded, these two friends
are found inseparable.   Whether in prosperity
or in adversity, in the Tower or on the scaffold,
Sir Walter always had his Fidus Achates to
look after him and watch his interests.   With
a sharp wit, close mouth, and ready pen Hariot
was of inestimable service to his liberal patron.
With rare attainments in the Greek and Latin
Classics, and all branches of the abstract sciences,
he combined that perfect fidelity and honesty of
character which placed him always above suspicion even of the enemies of Sir Walter.   He
was neither a politician nor statesman, and therefore could be even in those times a faithful guide,
philosopher, and friend to Raleigh.

In the year 1585, as has already been stated
above, Hariot, at the age of twenty-five, went
out to Virginia in Raleigh's 'first Colonie' as
surveyor and historiographer with Sir Richard
Grenville, and remained there one year under
Governor Ralph Lane, returning in July 1586,
in Sir Francis Drake's home-bound fleet from
the West Indies.   During the absence of this
expedition Raleigh had received triple favors
from Fortune.   He had entered Parliament,
been knighted, and had been presented by the
Queen with twelve thousand broad acres in Ireland.   These Irish acres were partly the Queen's
perquisite from the Babington 'conspiracy.'
Other royal windfalls had considerably in-
creased Sir Walter's expectations, and aroused
his ambition.   Hariot is known to have spent
some time in Ireland on Raleigh's estates there
during the reign of Elizabeth, but it is uncertain
when.   It may have been between the autumn
of 1586 and the autumn of 1588.   He was in
London in the winter of 1588-89 in time to get
out hurriedly his report in February 1589.   It

is possible, however, that he went to Ireland
after his book was out. He was probably the
manager of one of the estates there as Governor
John White was of another in 1591-93.

The next early author whom we find speaking of Hariot is his lifelong friend and companion Robert Hues or Hughes in his ' Tractatus de / Globis et eo- / rvm vsv, / Accommo-
datus iis qui Lon- / dini editi ſunt Anno 1593,/
ſumptibus Gulielmi Sanderſoni / Ciuis Londin-
enſis,/ Conſcriptus à Ro-/berto Hues./ Londini /
In ædibus Thomæ Dawſon. / 1594.' / 8°

In his dedication to Sir Walter Raleigh the
author says :

Borealiora Europæ noſtrates diligentiſſime luſtrarunt. Primo
Hugo Willoughby eques Anglus & Richardus Chanceler has
oras apperuerunt. Succedit eis Stephanus Borough, vlterius pro-
greſsi ſunt Arturus Pet & Carol. Iackman. Suſceptæ ſunt hæ
nauigationes, inſtigante Sebaſtiano Caboto, vt, ſiquâ poſset fieri
traiectum in regiones Synanum & Cathayæ breuiſſimum con-
ſequeremur, at irreto hæc omnia conatu, niſi quod his medijs
firmatum eſt commercium cum Moſchouitis. Hâc cum non
ſuccederet, inſtitutæ ſunt nauigationes ad Borealiora Americæ,
quas primo ſuscepit Martinus Frobiſher, ſecutus eſt poſtea
Ioannes Dauis. Ex his omnibus nauigationibus multi antiquiorum
errores, magna eorum ignorantia detecta eſt. Atque his conatibus
minus ſuccedentibus, gens noſtra nauibus abundans otij impa-

tiens, in alias partes fuas nauigationes inftituerunt. Humphredus
Gilbert Eques, Americæ oras Hifpanis incognitas, magno animo
& viribus, fucceffu non æquali noftris aperire conatus eft. Id
quod tuis poftea aufpicijs (vir honoratifsime) felicius fufceptum
eft quibus Virginia nobis patefacta eft, præfecto clafsis Richardo
Grinuil nobili equite, quam diligentifsime luftrauit & defcripfit
Thomæ Hariotus.

In the English edition of Robert Hues' work, London, 1638, this very interesting but somewhat irrelevant passage appears as follows:

Among whom, the first that adventured on the discovery of
these parts, were, Sir Hugh Willoughby, and Richard Chanceler:
after them, Stephen Borough. And farther yet then either of
these, did Arthur Pet, and Charles Iackman discover these parts.
And these voyages were all undertaken by the instigation of
Sebastian Cabot: that so, if it were possible, there might bee
found out a nearer pafsage to Cathay and China : yet all in
vane ; fave only that by this meanes a course of trafficke was
confirmed betwixt us and the Mofcovite.

When their attempts fucceeded not this way ; their next de-
signe was then to try, what might bee done in the Northern
Coasts of America : and the first undertaker of these voyages
was Mr. Martin Frobisher: who was afterward feconded by Mr.
Iohn Davis. By meanes of all which Navigations, many errours
of the Ancients, and their great ignorance was discovered.

But now that all these their endeavours fucceeded not, our
Kingdome at that time being well furnished in fhips, and im-
patient of idlenefse : they resolved at length to adventure upon
other parts. And first Sir Humphrey Gilbert with great courage and Forces attempted to make a discovery of those parts of
America, which were yet unknowne to the Spaniard : but the
succese was not answerable. Which attempt of his, was after-

ward more prosperously prosecuted by that honourable Gentleman Sir Walter Rawleigh : to whose meanes Virginia was first discovered unto us, the Generall of his Forces being Sir Richard Greenville : which Countrey was afterwards very exactly furveighed and described by Mr. Thomas Harriot.

This William Sanderson, the patron of Mollineux, Hood, and Hues, was a rich and liberal London merchant, who had married a niece of Raleigh. He contributed largely to Sir Walter's first reconnoitring expedition in 1584 under Amidas and Barlow, and was afterwards a liberal adventurer and supporter of Raleigh in all his colonial schemes. He was fond of the science of geography, and contributed largely to the preparation and publication of the globes of Mollineux, and the Descriptions of them by Hood and Hues in 1592 and 1594. He was also a good friend of all Raleigh's friends, and acted as Sir Walter's fiscal agent in regard to the Wine monopoly. On being called upon for a settlement of the large amount due, as Raleigh supposed, after his imprisonment in the Tower, Sanderson denied his indebtedness, was sued, cast into the debtors' jail,

1

and died in poverty. His son published severe comments against Raleigh.

Robert Hues, who was an intimate friend and associate of Hariot, was born at Hertford in 1554. He became a poor scholar at Brazen nose, and was afterwards at St Mary's Hall with Hariot. He took his degree of A.B. in 1579. He is said to have been a good Greek scholar, and after leaving the University travelled and became an eminent geographer and mathematician. He attracted the attention, probably through Raleigh, of that noble patron of learning Henry Percy, 9th Earl of Northumberland, who took him into his service, made him one of his scientific companions while in the Tower, supported him partly at Sion, intrusted him to instruct his children, and finally sent him to Oxford as tutor at Christ Church of his eldest surviving son, Algernon Percy, who on the death of his father on gunpowder treason day 1632, became the 10th Earl of Northumberland. Hues died at Oxford the 24th of May, 1632, and was buried in the cathedral of Christ Church, according to the inscription on his monument. He is mentioned by Chapman in his translation of Homer's Works [1616] as 'another right learned, honest, and entirely loved friend of mine.' See infra, p. 183.

In 1595 Hariot was mentioned as a distinguished man of science in his Seaman's Secrets by Captain John Davis the navigator, a friend and partner of Raleigh.

On the eleventh of July 1596 Hariot under peculiar circumstances wrote a long and confidential letter to Sir Robert Cecil, Chief Secretary of State, in the interests of Raleigh's Guiana projects. The letter is here given in full, as it shows better than anything else the close and confidential relations existing between Sir Walter and Hariot at that time. Raleigh had returned from Guiana, his first El Dorado expedition, in August 1595, and had in the mean time employed such energy and enterprise that within about five months he had fitted out and dispatched his second El Dorado fleet under his friend Captain Keymis. This second expedition returned to Plymouth in June 1596, a

few days after Raleigh had gone with Essex
and Howard of Effingham on that world-renowned expedition against Cadiz. Sir Walter
appears to have left his affairs in the hands of
his ever faithful Hariot, and hence this sensible
and timely letter in the absence of his patron.
There appears to have been no complaint against
Keymis ; but the master of his ship, Samuel
Mace, seems to have been less discreet. The letter tells its own story, and gives a vivid picture
of the intelligent earnestness of Sir Walter respecting Guiana, and at the same time the earnest
intelligence of Hariot during Raleigh's absence
in Spain.

It has been denied that Raleigh really expected to find the El Dorado in either his first
expedition of 1595 or last in 1617, but this letter goes to show that both he and Hariot had
firm faith in the scheme. Indeed in a German
book of travels just published, entitled ' Aus
den Llanos. Schildenung einer naturwissen-
schaftlichen Reise nach Venezuela, Von Carl
Sachs, Leipzig, 1879,' the writer states that the

export of gold from Spanish Guiana in 1875 was
79,496 ounces. He says that the richest mine,
that of Callao, has of late years returned as
much as 500 per centum. After briefly narra-
ting the expeditions of Raleigh, which had been
preceded by various Spanish expeditions, he
adds : 'Now at this day, after nearly three centuries, the riches sought for have been actually
found in the very country where these unfortunate efforts were made.' Hariot's letter is as
follows :

LETTER OF THOMAS HARIOT TO MR SECRETARY
SIR ROBERT CECIL.

From the original holograph in the Cecil Papers at Hatfield, vol. xliii,
As first printed in Edward Edward's Life of
Raleigh, vol. ii, page 420.

Right Honourable Sir,

   These are to let you understand that whereas, according to
your Honor's direction, I have been framing of a Charte out
of some such of Sir Walter's notes and writings, which he hath
left behind him,—his principal Charte being carried with him,
—if it may please you, I do thinke most fit that the discovery of Captain Kemish be added, in his due place, before I
finish it. It is of importance, and all Chartes which had that
coast before be very imperfecte, as in many thinges elce. And
that of Sir Walter's, although it were better in that parte then
any other, yet it was don but by intelligence from the Indians,
and this voyadge was specially for the discovery of the same ;

which is, as I find, well and sufficiently performed. And because the secrecy of these matters doth much importe her Majesty and this State, I pray let me be so bould as to crave that
the dispatch of the plotting and describing be don only by me
for you, according to the order of trust that Sir Walter left
with me, before his departure, in that behalf, and as he hath
usually don heretofore. If your Honor have any notes from
Sir Thomas Baskerville, if it may please you to make me ac-
quaynted with them, that which they will manifest of other
particularytyes then that before Sir Walter hath described shall
also be set downe.

Although Captain Kemish be not come home rich, yet he
hath don the speciall thing which he was injoined to do, as the
discovery of the coast betwixt the river of Amasones and
Orinico, where are many goodly harbors for the greatest ships
her Majesty hath and any nomber; wher there are great rivers,
and more then probability of great good to be don by them
for Guiana, as by any other way or to other rich contryes bor-
deringe upon it. As also, the discovery of the mouth of
Orinico it self,—a good harbor and free passage for ingresse and
egresse of most of the ordinary ships of England, above 3 hundred miles into the contry. Insomuch that Berreo wondred
much of our mens comming up so far; so that it seemeth they
know not of that passage. Nether could they, or can possibly,
find it from Trinidado; from whence usually they have made
their discoveryes. But if it be don by them the shortest way,
it must be done out of Spayne. Now, if it shall please her
Majesty to undertake the enterprise, or permitte it in her sub-
jectes, by her order, countenance, and authority, for the sup-
planting of those that are now gotten thither, I thinke it of
great importance to keepe that which is don as secretly as we
may, lest the Spaniardes learne to know those harbors and en-
trances, and worke to prevent us.

And because I understand that the master of the ship with
Captain Kemish is somewhat carelesse of this, by geving and

selling copyes of his travelles and plottes of discoveryes, I thought it my dutye to remember it unto your wisdome, that some order might be taken for the prevention of such inconveniences as may thereby follow : by geving authority to some Justice, or the Mayor, to call him before them, and to take all his writinges and chartes or papers that concerne this discovery, or any elce, in other mens handes, that he hath sold or conveyed them into ; and to send them sealed to your Honor, as also to take bond for his further secrecy on that behalf. And the like order to be taken by those others, as we shall further informe your Honor of, that have any such plots, which yet, for myne owne parte, I know not of ; or any other order, by sending for him up or otherwise, as to your wisdome shall seeme best.

Concerning the *Eldorado* which hath been shewed your Honor out of the Spanish booke of Acosta, which you had from Wright, and I have seene, when I shall have that favour as but to speake with you I shall shew you that it is not ours—that we meane—there being three. Nether doth he say, or meane, that Amazones river and Orinoco is all one,—as some, I feare, do averre to your Honor ; as by good profe out of that booke alone I can make manifest ; and by other meanes besides then this discovery, I can put it out of all dout.

To be breef, I am at your Honor's comandement in love and duty farther than I can sodeynly expresse for haste. I will wayte upon you at Court, or here at London, about any of these matters or any others, at any time, if I might have but that favour as to heare so much. I dare not presume of my selfe, for some former respectes. My fidelity hath never been impeached, and I take that order that it never shall. I make no application. And I beseech your Honor to pardon my boldness, because of haste. My meaning is allwayes good. And so I most humbly take my leave. This Sunday, 11th of July 1596.

Your Honor's most ready at commandement
in all services I may,

THO. HARRIOTE.

Addressed:
To the right honorable Sir ROBERT CICILL, Knight
    Principall Secretary to Her Majesty, these.
    Endorsed:
11 July, 1596.   Mr Harriott to my Master.

The vigilant Secretary lost no time in acting
upon Hariot's suggestions.   On the 31st of
July Sir George Trenchard and Sir Ralph
Horsey wrote to Cecil from Dorchester in reply
to his instructions, that they had seized the charts
and books of the 'India Voyage' [to Guiana]
from one Samuel Mace and William Downe,
which they would send up to the Secretary if desired.   They were desired, and accordingly sent
them by post on the 10th of August.   A few days
later Raleigh returned to Plymouth with the
first glorious news of the success of the English
fleet at Cadiz ; which news completely turned
the heads of the people of England one way, and
those of the Queen and the hungry politicians
the other.   Poor Mace, to whom Raleigh was
much attached, was restored to his confidence.
To Raleigh more than to any one man this
triumph over Spain was justly due, but in the

pitiful squabbles that followed in the apportion-
ment of the honors and the spoils Sir Walter
used to aver that his sole gain in this great
national enterprise from beginning to end was
but a lame leg. He might have added that the
business had gained for him the envy, malice
and all uncharitableness of those in high places.
In worldly wealth he was now comparatively
poor, and his fortunes were broken, though the
Queen at times, only at times, smiled on him.

At what precise time Hariot, who never deserted Raleigh, became acquainted with Henry
Percy, Earl of Northumberland, with whose
honored name, next to that of Sir Walter's, his
must ever be associated, does not as yet appear.
It is known, however, that there was an intimacy between Raleigh and Percy as early as
1586, when Sir Walter presented Percy with a
coat of mail on his going over to Flanders, and
soon after a bedstead made of cedar from Virginia; while the Earl about the same time gave
to Sir Walter a 'stroe coloured velvet saddle.'
From this time to the day of Raleigh's triumph

m

on the scaffold there exists plenty of evidence of their continued intimacy.

When therefore the Earl and Raleigh were finally caged together in the Tower for life in 1606 their friendship was of more than twenty years' standing. From this we infer that Hariot also knew Percy almost from the time of his joining Raleigh; but the earliest mention of his name in connection with that of the Earl which we have met with is this of 1596, in the Earl's pay-rolls, still preserved at Sion, and described in the Sixth Report of the Royal Commission of Historical Manuscripts, page 227, 'To Mr. Herytt for a book of the Turk's pictures, 7*s*.' It appears from the same rolls that from Michaelmas 1597 to 1610, if not earlier and later, an annual pension of £80 (not £120, or £150, or £300, as variously stated) was paid to Hariot by the Earl. This pension was probably continued as long as Hariot lived; and besides there are not wanting many marks of the Earl's liberality, friendship, and love for his companion and pensioner, who was long known as ' Hariot of Sion on Thames,' as

expressed on his monument. In the Earl's accounts for 1608 there is this entry, ' Payment
for repairing and finishing Mr Heriotts house
at Sion.'

At what time exactly Hariot took up his residence at Sion the Earl's new seat (purchased
of James in 1604) is not known, but probably
soon after the Earl was sent to the Tower in
1606. There is preserved a Letter from Sir
William Lower addressed to Hariot at Sion
dated the 30th of September 1607, and other
letters or papers exist showing his continued
residence there until near the time of his death
in 1621. Wood and many subsequent writers
to the present time have confused Sion near
Isleworth with Sion College in London. They
are totally distinct. Hariot had nothing to do
with Sion College, which was not founded until
1630, nine years after his death. The error
arose out of the coincidence of Torporley's taking chambers at Sion College on retiring from
his clerical profession, and dying there in April
1632, leaving his mathematical books and

manuscripts to the College Library. He had
been appointed by Hariot to look over, arrange,
and ' pen out the doctrine ' of his mathematical
writings. Torporley's abstracts of Hariot's papers are still preserved in Sion College Library.

What the Earl of Northumberland did for
Hariot is, as the world goes, ascribed to patron-
age; what Hariot did for the Earl cannot be
measured by money or houses, but may be summed up in four words, alike honorable to both,
' they were long friends.' To this day the debt
of gratitude from the philosopher to the nobleman is fairly balanced by the similar debt of the
nobleman to the philosopher. Hariot's Will,
given on pages 193-203, tells the rest of the
story of this noble friendship.

It is manifest, however, from many conside-
rations that the noble Earl took a lively and almost officious interest in the public honor and
character of his friend, for Hariot appears to
have been as careless of his own scientific reputation as his contemporary Shakspeare is said
to have been of his literary eminence.

On the other hand, Hariot's interest in the Earl's affairs and family at Sion redound greatly to his credit. He was both an eminent scholar and a remarkable teacher. Earnest students flocked to him for higher education from all parts of the country. Besides the private scientific and professional instruction that from the first he gave to Raleigh, his captains and sea officers, he seems to have had under his scientific tuition and mathematical guidance many young men who afterwards became celebrated; among whom may be mentioned Robert Sidney, the brother of Sir Philip, afterwards Lord Lisle of Penshurst; Thomas Aylesbury of Windsor, afterwards Sir Thomas, the great-grandfather of two queens of England; the late Lord Harrington; Sir William Protheroe and Sir William Lower of South Wales; Nathaniel Torporley of Shropshire; Sir Ferdinando Gorges of Devonshire; Captain Keymis; Captain Whiddon, and many others. Cordial and affectionate letters of most of these men to their venerated master are still preserved.

At Sion were the groves of Hariot's academy.

Yet he with Warner and Hues was constantly
passing by the Thames between Sion and the
Tower, some three or four hours by oar and tide.
They were all three pensioners, or in the pay,
of the Earl, though the last two were on a very
different footing from that of Hariot as to emoluments and responsible position. They were,
however, companions of both the Earl and Sir
Walter, and, if tradition is to be believed, they
were sometimes joined by Ben Jonson, Dr Bur-
rill, Rev. Gilbert Hawthorne, Hugh Broughton,
the poet Hoskins and perhaps others.

The Earl had a large family to be educated,
and there is reason to believe that in his absence
from Sion Hariot was intrusted for many years
with the confidential supervision of some of the
Earl's personal affairs at Sion, including the
education of his children. How he identified
himself with the noble family of his patron may
be inferred from these extracts from a letter to
Hariot, dated July 19, 1611, of William Lower,
one of his loving disciples. Cecil had been fishing out some new evidence of Percy's treason

from a discharged servant, and was pressing cruelly upon the prisoner. Lower writes :

I have here [in South Wales] much otium and therefore I may cast awaye some of it in vaine pursuites, chusing always rather to doe some thinge worth nothing then nothing att all. How farre I had proceeded in this, I ment now to have given you an account, but that the reporte of the unfortunate Erles relapse into calamitie makes me beleeve that you are enough troubled both with his misfortunes and my ladys troubles; and so a discourse of this nature would be unseasonable. [And concludes the letter with] But at this time this much is to much. I am sorrie to heare of the new troubles ther, and pray for a good issue of them especiallie for my ladys sake and her five litle ones. [The Countess of Northumberland here referred to was the mother of Sir William Lower's wife, who was Penelope Perrot, daughter of Sir John Perrot, who married Lady Dorothy Devereux, sister of Essex, and for her second husband Henry Percy the 9th Earl of Northumberland. Lower died in 1615.]

This responsible trust gave Hariot a good house and home of his own at Sion, with independence and an observatory. He had a library in his own house, and seems to have been the Earl's librarian and book selector or purchaser for the library of Sion House, as well as for the use of the Earl in the Tower. The Earl was a great book-collector, as appears by his pay-rolls. Books were carried from Sion to the Tower and back again, probably not only for

the Earl's own use, but for Raleigh's in his History of the World. Many of these books, it is understood, are still preserved at Petworth, then and subsequently one of the Earl's seats, but now occupied by the Earl of Leconsfield.

To look back a little. Before either Raleigh or Henry Percy was shut up in the Tower, we find one of Hariot's earliest and ablest mathematical disciples, Nathaniel Torporley, a learned clergyman, writing in high praise of him in his now rare mathematical book in Latin, entitled, 'Diclides Coelometricæ,' or Universal Gates of Astronomy, containing all the materials for calculation of the whole art in the moderate space of two tables, on a new general and very easy system. By Nathaniel Torporley, of Shropshire, in his philosophical retreat, printed in 1602. The exact title is as follows:

Diclides Coelometricæ / ſeu / Valvæ Astronomicæ / vniversales / Omnia artis totius numera Pſephophoretica in ſat modicis / finibus duarum Tabularum Methodo noua, generali, / & facilima continentes. / Authore Natha[le] Torporlaeo Salop-

ienſi / in ſeceſſu Philotheoro. / Londini / Excudebat Felix Kingston. 1602. / 4°.

In the long preface Torporley, who had entered St Mary's Hall the year Hariot gradua-
ted, and who during his travels abroad had
served two years as private secretary or amanu-
ensis to Francis Vieta, the great French Mathematician, but who had since become a disciple of
the greater English Mathematician, thus admir-
ingly speaks of his new master, Thomas Hariot:

Neque enim, per Authorum cunctationem & affectatam ob-
ſcuritatem, fieri potuit, vt in prima huius Artis promulgatione,
eidem alicui & inventionis laudem, & erudiendi mercedem de-
ferremus; ſed dimicantibus illis, neque de minoribus præmijs
quam de imperio Mathematico certantibus; muſſantibus verò
alijs, & arrectis animis expectantibus,

Quis pecori imperitet, quem tot armenta ſequantur;
non defuit Angliæ & ſuus Agonista (ornatiſſimum dico, et in
omni eruditionis varietate principem virum Thomam Hariotum,
hominē natū ad Artes illustrandas, &, quod illi palmariū erit præs-
tantiſſimū, ad nubes philoſophicas, in quibus multa iam ſecula
caligauit mundus, indubitatæ veritatis ſplendore diſcutiendas) qui
vetaret, tam ſolidæ laudis ſpolia ad exteros integra deuolui. Ille
enim (etiamdum in pharetra concluſa, quæ pupillā viuacis auiculæ
terebraret, ſagitta) ipſam totius Artis eius metam egregia methodo
collimauit; expedita verò facilitate patefactam, inter alios ami-
corum, & mihi quoque tradidit; multisꝗ vltro citroꝗ iactatis
Quæſtionibus, ingenia noſtra in abyſſo huius Artis exercendi
cauſam præbuit.

n

Of Mr Torporley we shall have more to say
further on, as he is particularly mentioned in
Hariot's will.   Meanwhile here is an attempt
at a translation of his peculiar Latin in the
above extract :

> For indeed by the delays and affected obscurity of authors, it
> was impossible, that in the first promulgation of the art, we
> should give the praise of invention and the credit of teaching,
> to the same individual ; but while they were quarrelling & con-
> tending for no less a prize than the empire of Mathematics, whilst
> others were muttering, and waiting with excited minds to see
>
> Who should rule the flock, whom so many herds should follow,
>
> our own champion has not been wanting to England. I mean
> Thomas Hariot, a most distinguished man, and one excelling
> in all branches of learning : a man born to illustrate Science,
> and, what was his principal distinction, to clear away by the
> splendour of undoubted truth those philosophical clouds in which
> the world had been involved for so many centuries : who did
> not allow the trophies of substantial praise to be wholly carried
> abroad to other nations.   For he (while the arrow, which was
> to hit the bull's-eye, was yet in the quiver) defined by an ad-
> mirable method the limits of all that science ; and showed it to
> me, amongst others of his friends, explained in an expeditious
> and simple manner ; and by proposing various problems to us,
> enabled us to exercise our ingenuity in the profundities of this
> science.

But time and space beckon.   On the 24th of
March 1603, set 'that bright occidental Star,'
and 'that mock Sun' frae the north took by suc-
cession its place.   To Raleigh the change was

the setting of a great hope, for to Queen Elizabeth he owed his fortunes, and was proud of the debt. To Raleigh more than to any other one man, notwithstanding his many faults, the Queen owed the brilliancy of her Court, the efficacy and terror of her navy, the enterprise and intelligent energy of her people, to say nothing of the adventurous spirit of colonization which he awoke in his efforts in Western Planting. The glory of his achievements today is the glory alike of England and English America. King James let no man down so far as he did Raleigh. Perhaps it was because there was no one left of Elizabeth's Court who could fall so far.

On three trumped up charges which never were, and never could be sustained with due form of law, Raleigh was with small delay thrown into the Tower. Several other noblemen and less eminent persons were sent there also. The Asiatic plague was raging in the City. A moral pestilence of equal virulence at the same time infested the Court. The State prisoners must be tried openly, though already secretly condemned. The Judges of his 'dread Majesty' dared not venture to the Tower as usual for the trials, forgetting apparently that its precincts were just as unhealthy for the great prisoners of State as for them, who were liable any day on the miffs of majesty to change places.

So it was determined that the 'traitors' should be carted down to Winchester for trial. A cold wet November seven-days' journey through mud and slush was the miserable dodge to carry out this scheme of darkness which neither Coke nor Popham would have dared to perpetrate in the broad light of London. It was, as all the world knows, a mock trial. The prisoners Raleigh, Cobham, Gray, and Markham were condemned and sentenced to death as traitors, and Raleigh, for the grim sport of the royal Nimrod, was made to witness a mock execution of his fellow-convicts, but being in due course all respited by a warrant which the Governor of Winchester Castle had carried three days in his pocket, were carted back to the Tower, where, not pardoned, their sentences not commuted, but simply deferred, they were tortured with a living death hanging over them, like the sword of Damocles depending on royal caprice.

Here Raleigh dragged out his long imprisonment, and (as tersely & truly expressed by his son) was, after thirteen years, beheaded for opposing the very thing he was condemned and sentenced for favouring. The whole story is a bundle of inconsistencies, like that of Henry Percy, the 9th Earl of Northumberland, committed to the Tower in 1606, and his fifteen years' imprisonment. The stories of these two celebrated men are inseparably connected with that of Hariot. But it is not our purpose to trace either Raleigh's or Percy's progress through these long and dreary years any further than is necessary to illustrate the life of Hariot, who was the light of the outer world to them both. Incarcerated and watched as they were, Hariot was the ears, the eyes, and the hands of these two noble captives.

The depth and variety of Hariot's intellectual and scientific resources, his honesty of purpose, his fidelity of character, his eminent scholarship, his unswerving integrity, and his command of tongue, rendered him alike invulnerable to politicians and to royal minions. He was with Raleigh at Winchester and in the Tower, off and on, as required, from 1604 to 1618, except during the last voyage to Guiana. He was at the same time a pensioner, a companion, and confidential factotum of his old friend the Earl of Northumberland both in the Tower and at Sion for fifteen years. Watched as these two prisoners were, ensnared, entrapped, and entangled for new evidence against them, it was necessary for Hariot to pursue a delicate and cautious course, to eschew politics, statecraft and treason, and to devote himself to pure science (almost the only pure commodity that was then a safeguard) metaphysics, natural philosophy, mathematics, history, and literature. He was their jackal, their book of reference, their guide, their teacher, and their friend.

Raleigh found himself in December 1603, lodged in the Tower, innocent, as is now generally admitted, of the charges against him, but legally attainted of high treason. All his worldly effects therefore escheated to the Crown. The King out of pure cowardice (for he dared not carry out the sentence of the Court) waived the horrid parts of the sentence—too horrid even to be quoted here—and commuted it to execution by the block. He also waived the immediate forfeiture of property acquired under Elizabeth's reign, and even allowed Raleigh to complete the entail of certain estates to his wife and son.

The Governor of the Tower and his Lieutenant were at first officially kind and friendly, extending many privileges to win his confidence. If there had been any treason in Sir Walter they would most certainly have wormed it out of him, for his eyes at first were not fully open. He still believed in the honour and fidelity of his mock friends at Court.

When no more satisfactory evidence of his guilt could be smuggled out of him, or his companions, in support of the unjust verdict, they began, in 1605, to abridge his privileges and darken his lights. At first his friends and visitors were cut down to a fixed number. There is a list among the Burleigh papers in the British Museum by which it appears that Lady Raleigh, her maid, and her son might visit Sir Walter. For this they took a house on Tower Hill near the old fortress, where they lived six years, or as long as this privilege lasted.

Then Sir Walter was to be allowed two men servants and a boy, who were to remain within the Tower. Besides these he was permitted to see on occasion, Mr Hawthorne, a clergyman; Dr Turner, his physician; Mr Johns, his surgeon; Mr Sherbery, his solicitor; his bailiff at Sherburne; and his old friend, Thomas Hariot, with no official designation.

It needs no ears under the walls of the Tower to tell us what were the duties of this learned and trusted friend, who had been Sir Walter's confidential factor for a quarter of a century in all his most important enterprises. Hariot, it will be perceived, was the only one named, in this house-list, without an assigned profession. Fortunately there is still preserved a 'hoggeshead of papers' in Hariot's handwriting, ill-assorted and hither-to unsifted, which partially reveal the secrets of this prison-house, and show Hariot here, there, and everywhere, mixed up with all the studies, toils, experiments, books, and literary ventures of our honored traitor.

So passed, with tantalizing uncertainty, the year 1605, with many fears for the future and some hopes; but 1606 brought into the Tower Sir Walter's old friend Henry Percy, another 'traitor.' With him, at first, there was consider-able liberality on the part of the officials (all paid for), and both Raleigh and Percy had each a garden to cultivate and walk in, and a still-room or laboratory in which to study and perform their 'magic.' Hariot was the master of both in these occult sciences. The 'furnace' and the 'still' were at first Raleigh's chief amusement and study. Assaying and transfusing metals, distill-ing simples and compounds, concocting medi-cines, and testing antidotes, with exercises in chemistry and alchemy, were the studies of both

o

Raleigh and the Earl. But soon the policy of the
Court changed. The prisoners had less liberty
and saw less of each other, and so the stills were
pulled down, and the gardens given up. Raleigh was more closely watched, and entrapped.
Then there was fencing and defencing, for nothing could stand against the King's persistent
rancor, and Cecil's dissimulation. From time to
time Sir Walter's titles, his offices, his Eliza-
bethan monopolies and his appointments were
all taken from him. All his emoluments were
wanted for hungry favourites; and finally the
Sherburne estate which he had been permitted
to entail on his son went by no higher law than
the king's, ' I mon hae it for Carr.'

During all these anxious months Hariot was
Sir Walter's close-mouthed and trusted Mercury, a silent messenger who floated frequently
by the tide on the Thames between the Tower
and his residence at Sion, a pensioner of, and
one of Percy's staff of wise men, but really
Raleigh's strong right hand. He adroitly and
faithfully served two masters, preserving his own

independence and self reliance, and not losing
the confidence of either.

From the trial at Winchester to the final
transfer of Sherburne, a period of some five
years, every step against Raleigh was taken
through the high Courts of Justice. That the
cannie monarch was capable of all this moral
wrong and legal crookedness need not surprise
any one who has investigated his antecedents
and proclivities, but that he on coming to England should have developed that masterly power
of warping great minds and bending the English Courts of Justice to his purposes, and even
crunching its strong old oaken Bench and Bar
into his own royal privy pocket, does surprise
one. The secret of this unenglish strength,
however, has been attributed partly to his Burleigh help.

When Raleigh found the cords thus tighten-
ing round him, he offered sundry concessions
and services for life and liberty. He would
carry out his schemes for enriching the king and
the kingdom by conquering and exploring Gui-

ana ; he would accept exile in Holland ; or
emigrate to Virginia, and help to build up a new
English empire in the West ; but all in vain. It
was feared that his unexpired and dormant patent might interfere with the King's own Virginia
charter.   So Raleigh and Hariot worked on,
but relieved the tedium by ever changing study.
Every year or two, as long as he could command
through himself or friends the resources, Raleigh
sent privately a reconnoitring and intelligence
ship to Guiana, to keep that pet enterprise alive.
In this delicate matter Hariot was Sir Walter's
geographer and assayer, while Hariot's old college friend, Keymis, was his factor or shipping
agent.

Then come Raleigh's Essays and smaller
writings, with his hopeful correspondence with the
Queen and Prince Henry. Lady Raleigh's privileges, after six years, ceased in 1611 ; probably
about the time that Cecil was for some unaccount-
able reason prospecting actively for new evidence
against both Sir Walter and Percy. The years
1610 and 1611 were anxious times for them

both; but they were bright days for Hariot, with his invention of the telescope and his discoveries.

Whether in the Tower, administering new scientific delicacies and delights to the prisoners; or at Sion, unlocking the secrets of the starry firmament by night, in his observatory; or floating between Sion and the Tower by day on the broad bosom of the Thames, prying into the optical secrets of lenses, and inventing his perspective trunks by which he could bring distant objects near, Hariot in foggy England of the north was working out almost the same brilliant series of discoveries that Galileo was making in Italy. To this day, with our undated and indefinite material, even with the new and much more precise evidence now for the first time herewith produced, it is difficult to decide which of them first invented the telescope, or first by actual observation with that marvellous instrument confirmed the truth of the Copernican System by revealing the spots on the Sun, the orbit of Mars, the horns of Venus, the satellites of Jupiter, the mountains in the Moon, the elliptical orbits of comets, *etc*. It is manifest, however, that they were both working in the same groove and at the same time.

Hariot was undoubtedly as great a mathematician and astronomer as Galileo. In 1607 at Ilfracombe and in South Wales, he had taken by hand and Jacob's staff, the old patriarchal method, valuable observations of the comet of that year, and compared notes with his astronomical pupil William Lower, and afterwards with Kepler. This comet, now known as Halley's, ought perhaps to have been named Hariot's, for it confirmed his notions that the motions of the planets were not perfect circles and afforded probably the germ of his reasoning out the elliptical orbits of comets, especially after his friend and correspondent [see infra, pages 178-180] Kepler's book *de Motibus Stellæ Martis* came out in 1609, and he had invented and improved his telescope or perspective 'truncke' or cylinder in 1609-10.

It is not positively stated that Hariot held direct correspondence with Galileo in 1609 and 1610 or even later, but the evidence is strong

that he was promptly kept informed of what was
going on in Italy in astronomical and mathematical discovery, as well as in Germany and
elsewhere. That he was using a ' perspective
truncke' or telescope as early as the winter of
1609-10, and that his ' servaunte' Christopher
Tooke (or as Lower in 1611 familiarly called
him 'Kitt') made lenses for him and fitted them
into his 'trunckes' for sale by himself, is known.

From this circumstance, and from the fact that
he disposed of many ' trunckes ' by his will, and
left a considerable stock of them to Tooke, it is
manifest that he manufactured and traded in telescopes from 1609 to 1621. With his invention
of the telescope then it required no correspondence with Galileo to induce him to rake the
heavens and sweep our planetary system for new
astronomical discoveries. To an astronomer of
his activity and mathematical acumen these discoveries followed as a matter of course. Like
Galileo he may have borrowed from the Dutch
(or quite as likely they of him) the idea that
by a combination of lenses it was possible to

bring distant objects near, but that he worked out
the idea independently of Galileo admits hardly
of a doubt. But he seems to have been less ambi-
tious than Galileo to claim priority in either the
invention or the discoveries that immediately followed. In this connection the following hitherto
unpublished letter will be read with interest :

LETTER OF SIR WILLIAM LOWER *in South Wales to*
THOMAS HARIOT *at Sion* 21 *June* 1610.
Printed from the holograph original in the British Museum

I gaue your letter a double welcome, both because it came
frõ you and contained newes of that strange nature ; although
that wch I craued, you haue deserued till another time.   Me
thinkes my diligent Galileus hath done more in his three fold
discouerie then Magellane in openinge the streightes to the
South sea or the dutch men that weare eaten by beares in Noua
Zembla. I am sure with more ease and saftie to him selfe and
more pleasure to mee. I am so affected with this newes as I
wish sommer were past that I mighte obserue these phenomenes
also. in the moone I had formerlie observed a strange spotted-
nesse al ouer, but had no conceite that anie parte therof mighte
be shadowes ; since I haue obserued three degrees in the darke
partes, of wch the lighter sorte hath some resemblance of
shadinesse but that they grow shorter or longer I cannot yet
pceaue. ther are three starres in Orion below the three in his
girdle so neere togeather as they appeared vnto me alwayes like
a longe starre, insomuch as aboute 4 yeares since I was a writing
you newes out of Cornwall of a view a strange phenomenon but
asking some that had better eyes then my selfe they told me,
they were three starres lying close togeather in a right line. thes
starres with my cylinder this last winter I often observed, and

it was longe er I beleued that I saw them, they appearinge through the Cylinder so farre and distinctlie asunder that without I can not yet disseuer. the discouerie of thes made me then obserue the 7 starres also in, ♉, wch before I alwayes rather beleued to be, 7. then euer could nomber them. through my Cylinder I saw thes also plainelie and far asunder, and more then, 7. to, but because I was prejugd with that number, I beleved not myne eyes nor was carefull to obserue how manie; the next winter now that you have opened mine eyes you shall heare much frō me of this argument. of the third and greatest (that I confesse pleased me most) I have least to say, sauing that just at the instante that I receaved your letters wee Traventane Philosophers were a consideringe of Kepler's* reasons by wch he indeauors to ouerthrow Nolanus and Gilberts opinions concerninge the immensitie of the Spheare of the starres and that opinion particularlie of Nolanus by wch he affirmed that the eye beinge placed in anie parte of the Univers the apparence would be still all one as vnto us here. When I was a sayinge that although Kepler had sayd somethinge to moste that mighte be vrged for that opinion of Nolanus, yet of one principall thinge hee had not thought ; for although it may be true that to the ey placed in anie starre of, ♋, the starres in Capricorne will vanish, yet he hath not therfore so soundlie concluded (as he thinkes) that therfore towards that parte of the world ther wilbe a voidnesse or thin scattering of little starres wheras els round about ther will appeare huge starres close thruste togeather : for sayd I (hauinge heard you say often as much) what is in that huge space betweene the starres and Saturne, ther remaine euer fixed infinite nombers wch may supplie the apparence to the eye that shalbe placed in ♋, wch by reason of ther lesser magnitudes doe flie our sighte what is aboute ♄. ♃. ♂. etc. ther moue other planets also wch appeare not. just as I was a saying this comes your letter, wch when I had redd, loe, qd I, what I spoke probablie experience hath made good ; so that we both with wonder and delighte fell a consideringe your letter, we

* pag. 106. de Noua Stella Serpentarii.

P

are here so on fire with thes thinges that I must renew my request and your promise to send mee of all sortes of thes Cylinders. my man shal deliuer you monie for anie charge requisite, and contente your man for his paines and skill.   Send me so manie as you thinke needfull vnto thes obseruations, and in requitall, I will send you store of observations.   Send me also one of Galileus bookes if anie yet be come ouer and you can get them. Concerning my doubte in Kepler, you see what it is to bee so far frō you.   What troubled me a month you satisfyed in a minute.   I have supplied verie fitlie my wante of a spheare, in the desolution of a hogshead, for the hopes therof haue framed me a verie fine one.   I pray also at your leasure answere the other pointes of my last letter concerning Vieta, Kepler and your selfe. I have nothinge to presente you in counter, but gratitude with a will in act to be vsefull vnto you and a power in proxima potentia ; wᶜʰ I will not leaue also till I haue broughte ad actum. If you in the meane time can further it, tell wher in I may doe you seruice, and see how wholie you shall dispose of me.

Your most assured and louing friend

Tra'uenti the longest day of, 1610.   Wiᴌᴌm Lowër.

Addressed: To his espesial good frind

Mʳ. Tʜᴏᴍᴀꜱ Hᴀʀʀɪᴏᴛ

Seal
of
Arms.

(*B. M. Add.* 6789.)   at Sion neere London.

[Tra'venti or Trafenty, near Lower Court, is eight or nine miles south-west of Caermarthen, near the confluence of the rivers Taf and Cywyn.]

The writer is fortunately able to throw some light upon these letters of Lower to Hariot.   In the *Monatliche Correspondenz*, vol. 8, 1803, published by F. X. von Zach at Gotha, pages 47-56, is a most interesting fragment of an original letter in English to Hariot. Dr Zach says that he found this letter at Petworth in 1784, and it being without date or signature he confidently assigned its authorship to the Earl of Northumberland, and guessed the date to have been prior to 1619. In his many notes he is in raptures over his discovery, and deplores the misfortune of its breaking off in the most interesting place just as the Earl was about to announce the discovery of the elliptical orbit of the comet of 1607, as reasoned out of Hariot's observations and the writings of Kepler. This famous letter has been used or copied in many places, particularly in Ersch and Gruber's Algemeine Encyklopädie under Hariot.

The mystery is now solved by giving here the letter in full. It is even more important than Dr Zach with all his enthusiasm supposed. It is not, however, from the pen of Northumberland, though none the less interesting on that account. The letter is in the well-known handwriting of Lower, of Tra'venti, on Mount Martin, near Llanfihangel, in South Wales, to his dearly loved friend and master Hariot at Sion, and is dated the 6th of February, 1610. The letter fills two sheets of foolscap paper. The first sheet of four pages Dr Zach found at Petworth, and it is to be hoped that it still exists there. The other sheet of four pages is preserved in the British Museum (Add. 6789). How long these two sheets have been separated it is difficult to tell, but probably from Hariot's day, that is, for more than two centuries and a half. The two fragments are now brought together and printed for the first time complete, the first half from Dr Zach's text, and the latter half copied verbatim direct from the original autograph manuscript, Brit. Mus. Add. 6789.

LETTER FROM SIR WILLIAM LOWER MATHEMATICIAN
AND ASTRONOMER TO THOMAS HARIOT AT SION
FEBRUARY 6, 1610.

I have receeved the perfpective Cylinder that you promifed me and am forrie that my man gave you not more warning, that I might have had alfo the 2 or 3 more that you mentioned to chufe for me. Hence forward he fhall have order to attend you better and to defray the charge of this and others, that he forgot to pay the worke man. According as you wifhed I have obferved the Mone in all his changes. In the new I difcover manifeftlie the earthfhine, a little before the Dichotomie, that fpot which reprefents unto me the Man in the Moone (but without a head) is firft to be feene. a little after neare the

brimme of the gibbous parts towards the upper corner appeare
luminous parts like ftarres much brighter then the reft and the
whole brimme along, lookes like unto the Defcription of Coafts
in the dutch bookes of voyages. in the full fhe appeares like
a tarte that my Cooke made me the laft Weeke. here a vaine
of bright ftuffe, and there of darke, and so confufedlie al over.
I muft confeffe I can fee none of this without my cylinder.
Yet an ingenious younge man that accompanies me here often,
and loves you, and thefe ftudies much, fees manie of thefe
things even without the helpe of the inftrument, but with it
fees them moft plainielie. I meane the younge Mr. Protheröe.

Kepler I read diligentlie. but therein I find what it is to be
fo far from you. For as himfelf, he hath almoft put me out
of my wits. his Aequanes, bis fections of excentricities, libra-
tions in the diameters of Epicycles, revolutions in Ellipfes, have
fo thoroughlie feafed upon my imagination as I do not onlie
ever dreame of them, but oftentimes awake lofe my felfe, and
power of thinkinge with to much wantinge to it. not of his
caufes for I cannot phanfie thofe magnetical natures. but aboute
his theorie which me thinks (although I cannot yet overmafter
manie of his particulars) he eftablifheth foundlie and as you fay
overthrowes the circular Aftronomie.

Do you not here ftartle, to fee every day fome of your inventions taken from you ; for I remember long fince you told me
as much, that the motions of the planets were not perfect
circles. So you taught me the curious way to obferve weight
in Water, and within a while after Ghetaldi comes out with it
in print. a little before Vieta prevented [anticipated] you of the
gharland of the greate Invention of Algebra. al thefe were your
deues and manie others that I could mention ; and yet to great
refervedneffe had robd you of thefe glories. but although the
inventions be greate, the first and last I meane, yet when I
furvei your ftorehoufe, I fee they are the smalleft things and
fuch as in comparifon of manie others are of fmal or no value.
Onlie let this remember you, that it is poffible by to much

procraftination to be prevented in the honor of fome of your rareft inventions and fpeculations. Let your Countrie and frinds injoye the comforts they would have in the true and greate honor you would purchafe your felfe by publifhing fome of your choife workes, but you know beft what you have to doe. Onlie I, becaufe I wish you all good, wifh this, and fometimes the more longinglie, because in one of your letters you gave me fome kind of hope therof.

But againe to Kepler I have read him twice over curforidlie. I read him now with Calculation. Some times I find a difference of minutes, fometimes falfe prints, and fometimes an utter confufion in his accounts. thefe difficulties are fo manie, and often as here againe I want your conference, for I know an hower with you, would advance my ftudies more than a yeare heare, to give you a taft of fome of thes difficulties that you may judge of my capacitie, I will fend you onlie this one [upon the *Locum Martis* out of Kepler's Astronomy, de motibus Stellæ Martis, etc.   Pragae, 1609, folio Ch. xxvi, page 137.]   For this theorie I am much in love with thefe particulars ;

1º his permutation of the medial to the apparent motions, for it is more rational that all dimenfions as of Eccentricities, apogacies, etc. . . . . fhould depend rather of the habitude to the fun, then to the imaginarie circle of orbis annuus.

2º His elliptical iter planetarum. for me thinks it fhews a Way to the folving of the unknown walks of comets.   For as his Ellipfis in the Earths motion is more a circle [*here endeth Dr Zach's fragment, and here beginneth the continuation from the original in the British Museum*] and in Mars is more longe and in some of the other planets may be longer againe so in thos commets that are appeard fixed the ellipsis may be neere a right line.

3. His phanfie of ecliptica media or his via regia of the sun, vnto wch the walke of al the other planets is obliq₃ more or lesse ; even the ecliptica uera under wch the earth walkes his yeares journie; by wch he solues handsomelie the mutation of the starres latitudes.   Indeed I am much delighted with his booke, but he

is so tough in manie places as I cannot bite him. I pray write
me some instructions in your next, how I may deale with him
to ouermaster him for I am readie to take paines, te modo jura
dantem indigeo, dictatorem exposco. But in his booke I am
much out of loue with thes particulars. 1. First his manie and
intollerable atechnies, whence deriue thos manie and vncertaine
assayes of calculation. 2. His finding fault with Vieta for mend-
ing the like things in Ptol: Cop. . . . . but se the justice Vieta
speakes sleightlie of Copernicus a greater then Atlas. Kepler
speakes as slightlie of Vieta, a greater then Appollonius whom
Kepler everie wher admires. For whosoever can doe the things
that Kepler cannot doe, shalbe to him great Appollonius. But
enough of Kepler let me once againe intreate your counsel how
to read him with best profit, for I am wholie possessed with
Astronomical speculations and desires. For your declaration of
Vieta's appendicle it is so full and plaine, as you haue aboundant-
lie satisfyed my desire, for wch I yield you the thankes I ought,
onlie in a word tell me whether by it he can solue Copernicus,
5 cap: of his 5. booke. The last of Vieta's probleames you
leaue to speake of because (you say) I had a better of you, w^ch
was more vniuersal and more easilie demonstrated, and findeth
the point, ε. as wel out of the plaine of the triangle giuen, as
in the plaine. I pray here helpe my memorie or vnderstand-
inge, for although I haue bethought my selfe vsq₃ ad insaniam.
I cannot remember or conceaue what proposition you meane.
If I haue had such a one of you, tel me what one it is and by
what tokens I may know it ; If I haue not had, then let me
now haue it, for you know how much I loue your things and
of all wayes of teaching for richnesse and fullnesse for stuffe
and forme, yours vnto me are incomparablie most satisfactorie.
If your leasure giue you leaue imparte also unto me somewhat
els of your riches in this argument.

Let me intreate you to advise and direct this bearer M^r.
Vaughan wher and how to prouide himselfe of a fit sphere ;
that by the contemplation of that our imaginations here may

be releued in manie speculations that perplexe our vnderstand-
ings with diagrammes in plano. He hath monie to prouide doe
you but tell him wher the are to be had and what manner of
sphere (I meane with what and how manie circles) wilbe most
vsefull for vs to thes studies.   After all this I must needs tell you
my sorrowes. God that gaue him, hath taken from me my onlie
sun, by continual and strange fits of Epelepsie or Apolexie, when
in apparence, as he was most pleasant and goodlie, he was moſt
healthie, but amongst other things, I haue learnt of you to setle
and submit my desires to the will of god ; onlie my wife with
more greife beares this affliction, yet now againe she begins to
be comforted. Let me heare frõ you and according to your
leasure and frindshippe haue directions in the course of studie I
am in. Aboue al things take care of your health, keepe correspondence with Kepler and wherinsoeuer you can haue vse of
me, require it with all libertie.   Soe I rest ever,

>   Your assured and true friend to be vsed in
>   all things that you please.

>   Wiłłm Lowër.

Tra'vent on Mount Martin [in South Wales.]
       6 February, 1610.

   Let me not make my selfe more able then ther is cause.   I
can not order the calculation by the construction you sent me
of Vieta's 3. probleme, to find the distances of c. & d. & b.
from the Apogeñ or the proportion of ia. to ac. the eccentricitie.
I tooke Copernicus, 3. observations in the, 6. chap. of his, 5.
booke, therfore helpe here once againe.

   Addressed : To his especiall good friend

>   Mr. Tho : Harryot at Sion neere London.

About this time, it is understood, Raleigh took up seriously and earnestly the great literary work of his life, *The History of the World*. It must

have been brewing in his mind for years, for in
his preface he expressed the fears he had enter-
tained 'that the darkness of age and death would
have overtaken him long before the performance.'
The work, according to Camden, was published
in April 1614, just before the meeting of Parliament. It appeared anonymously, and for ob-
vious reasons was not entered at Stationers'
Hall. James is said to have had his conscience
so pricked by certain passages which everywhere
pervade the work on the power, conduct and
responsibility of princes, that strenuous efforts
were made in January 1615 to call in and sup-
press it, but the king might as well have attempted to call back a departed spirit by Act of
Parliament as to call in that 'History of the
World' by royal proclamation. The Book was
in type and in the hands of the people of England. It could therefore no more be suppressed
at that day by princely power than could manifest
destiny itself. The second edition of 1621 was
the first with Raleigh's name.

This grand work, which in almost every chap-

ter shows the masterly hand of Raleigh himself,
needs no comment here.   It is however no dis-
paragement of the book (but the contrary) to say
that in the collection, arrangement and conden-
sation of its materials; that in unlocking the mu-
niment room of antiquity and perusing the chief
authors of the Greek and Latin classics from
Heroditus to Livy and Eusebius, covering a period
of near four thousand years, he must have had
at cheerful beck powerful and competent aid.
To collect, read, collate, note down, and digest
these vast and scattered treasures into reasonable and presentable shape for the master mind,
required not a bevy of poets and parsons, but one
masterly scholar of scientific, analytic, mathematical, philosophical and religious training.
Such a man was Hariot.

We read of Gibbon's twenty years' fag and
toil on the materials of the History of the Roman Empire alone, and at a time when there
were many aids not existing in Raleigh's day.
Gibbon personally ransacked the libraries of
Europe.   Raleigh had scarcely four years to

cover the four most ancient empires and a much longer period, and was himself confined to Tower Hill. But he had at command a Hariot, a sort of winged Mercury, who was neither entowered nor hide-bound with conceit or ignorance. He was a marvellously good Greek and Latin scholar, who wrote Latin with almost as much ease as English. One has but to read the vast number of notes, citations and particular references in the History of the World to see the height, depth, and perfect modelling of the structure.

Raleigh was unquestionably the designer, the architect and the finisher of his History of the World. To him is due the honor and credit of the work. But who was the builder? The answer manifestly is Thomas Hariot of Sion on Thames, learned, patient, self-forgetting, painstaking, long-waiting, devoted Hariot. Many writers have claimed to be, or have been named as, Sir Walter's assistants and polishers. Ben Jonson, Rev. Dr Burhill, John Hoskins the poet, and others have each had their advocates, but without sufficient evidence. It may well be questioned if any one of them possessed either the ability, the time, the access to the Tower, or the opportunity to perform such herculean labors of love. These claims are apparently all based on pure conjecture, or unrectified gossip, as shown by Mr Bolton Corney in his razorly reply to Mr Isaac D'Israeli. But Thomas Hariot, on the contrary, possessed abundantly what they all lacked, the necessary credentials. For proof of this assertion the doubter, as well as the lover of confirmed historical accuracy, is referred to the Hariot papers still preserved partly at Petworth and partly in the British Museum.

The Hariot manuscripts, of which there are thousands of folio pages all in his own handwriting, seem to be still in the same confused state in which he left them. He directed that the 'waste' should be weeded out of his mathematical papers and destroyed. But this duty seems, fortunately for us, to have been neglected by his executors, and hence among this 'waste' one has even now no great difficulty in recognizing in the well-known Latin handwriting of

the 'magician,' many jottings in chronology, geography and science, and many abstracts and citations of the classics, that in their time must have
played parts in the *History of the World*. The
Will now first produced lets in a flood of light on
the history of these valued papers, and dispels
a great deal of the heaps of foreign pretension,
domestic assertion, and mixed charlatanism that
have since 1784 beclouded the memories of both
Raleigh and Hariot. It is true that on a hint
in the previous century from Camden of a will
by the great mathematician, many conjectures
were afloat from the days of Pell, Collins, Wallis
and Wood, but it has not been possible until now
for one, with due knowledge of the main events
in the lives of these two men, each equally great
in his own sphere, to satisfactorily clear away
any considerable portion of the misconception and
misstatements of biographers and historians concerning them and their achievements. The dawn
however is coming, when these new materials
now first printed by the Hercules Club, but not
worked up, may attract the attention of some

historian competent to give them a thorough scientific scrutiny and ' pen their doctrine.'

It is not our purpose here to dwell upon Raleigh's masterpiece. From the preface of the *History of the World*, which opens with ' the boundless ambition of mortal man,' to the epilogue which closes up the work with the glorious triumph of Death, the whole book is replete with lessons of wisdom and warning. No one can rise from its perusal without perceiving that the modern author has made himself by apt illustration an accomplished actor in ancient history, while the ancient characters are made in their vera effigies to strut on modern stages. His pictures of great actions and great men, noble deeds and nobler princes, are drawn with such masterly perspective of truth, that they serve for all time ; while his portraiture of tyrants, villains, and dishonorable characters are no less lifelike and human. One marvels not therefore that King James, whose political creed was that the people are bound to princes by iron, and princes to the people by cobwebs, should see in

Raleigh's portraiture of the upright kings no likeness to himself, but had no difficulty in recognizing in the deformed greatness and selfish virtues of the old monarchs qualities suggestive of himself and his favorites. This grand history, extending from the creation over the four great monarchies of the world, near four thousand years, closes with the final triumph of Emilius Paullus in these memorable and oft-repeated words from the first edition of 1614.

Kings and Princes have alwayes laid before them, the actions, but not the ends, of those great Ones which præceded them. They are alwayes transported with the glorie of the one, but they never minde the miserie of the other, till they finde the experience themselves. They neglect the advice of God, while they enioy life, or hope it; but they follow the counsell of Death, upon his first approach. It is he that puts into man all the wisdome of the world, without speaking a word; which God with all the words of His Law, promises, or threats, doth not infuse. Death which hateth and destroyeth man, is beleeved; God, which hath made him and loves him, is alwayes deferred. I have considered, saith Solomon, all the workes that are under the Sunne, and behold, all is vanitie and vexation of spirit: but who beleeves it, till Death tells it us. It was Death, which opening the conscience of Charles the fift, made him enjoyne his sonne Philip to restore Navarre; and King Francis the First of France, to command that justice should be done upon the murderers of the Protestants in Merindol and Cabrieres, which till then he neglected. It is therefore Death alone that can suddenly make man know himselfe. He tells the proud and insolent, that they are but Abjects, and humbles them at the instant ; makes them crie, complaine, and repent ; yea, even to hate their forepassed happinesse.   He takes the account of the rich, and proves him a beggar, a naked begger, which hath interest in nothing, but in the grauell that filles his mouth. He holds a glasse before the eyes of the most beautifull, and makes them see therein their deformitie and rottennesse ; and they acknowledge it.

O eloquent, just and mightie Death ! whom none could advise, thou hast perswaded ; what none hath dared, thou hast done ; and whom all the world hath flattered, thou onely hast cast out of the world and despised : thou hast drawne together all the farre stretched greatnesse, all the pride, crueltie, and ambition, of man, and covered it all over with those two narrow words : *Hic jacet.*

With this outburst of true eloquence the historian of the world laid down his pen in 1614. Four short years later the same historian himself, wickedly sacrificed by his hispaniolized monarch, laid down his life on the scaffold, with an apotheosis scarcely less eloquent. No death recorded in ancient or modern history is more grand or instructive than that of Sir Walter Raleigh, in many respects the greatest man of his age.

On the execution being granted in the King's Bench Court, on the afternoon of the 28th of October 1618, he asked for a little time for preparation, but his request was refused, Bacon having already in his pocket the death warrant duly signed by the King before the meeting of the Court! Sir Walter then asked for paper, pen and ink; and when he came to die that he might be permitted to speak at his farewell. To these last requests he appears to have received no reply, but was with indecent haste hustled off to the Gate House for execution early the next morning, the 29th of October, Lord Mayor's day, when it was expected that the crowd would go cityward. However, there was a crowd, and probably in consequence he was not prohibited from speaking. He had prepared himself, and is said to have consulted a '*Note of Remembrance*' which he held in his hand while speaking. It is possible, nay, probable that this very same *Note* still survives in 'paper-saving' Hariot's 'waste,' for a precious little waif, all crumpled and soiled, just such a 'Note of Remembrance,' it is believed, as Raleigh held in his hand and consulted during that ever memorable speech, has come down to us, and is now preserved among the Hariot papers in

r

the British Museum. It has been recently recognized and identified by Mr Stevens, who has
placed it, with other newly discovered documents
respecting our philosopher, at the disposition of
the Hercules Club. It is thought to possess in-
ternal evidence of having been drawn out *before*
the speech, and is not therefore Hariot's jottings
of remembrance *after* it. But positive proof is
wanting.

It is beyond all doubt, however, in the well-
known handwriting of Hariot, and is presumed
to be the 'note of remembrance' *for* the speech,
made in the Gate House, probably from dictation,
during the night before the execution. It appears
as if hurriedly penned with a blunt quill, and is
on a narrow strip of thin foolscap paper such as
Hariot used. It is about twelve inches long and
nearly four inches wide, about one-third of the
lower part of the paper being blank. There is
no heading, date, or anything else on the paper.
It is rather difficult to read, but every word,
letter and point have been made out, and the
whole *Note* is here given, line for line, and ver-

batim, the heading and press-mark only being
added :

[SIR WALTER RALEIGH'S ' NOTE OF REMEMBRANCE '
for his speech on the Scaffold Oct. 29 1618.]

Two fits of an agew.
Thankes to god.
of calling god to witness.
note
That He Speake iustly & truely.

1.) Concerning his loyalty to y^e
King.   French Agent,
& Comiſſion frō y^e
french King.

2.) of Slanderous ſpeeches touching
his maj^ty.   a french man.
Sr L. Stukely.

3.) Sr L. Stukely.   My lo: Carewe.
4.) Sr L. Stukely.   My lo: of Danchaster.
5.) Sr L. St: Sr Edward Perham.
6.) Sr L. St.   A letter on london hyway
10000^li.

7.) Mine of Guiana.
8.) Came back by conſtreynt.
9.) My L. of Arundell.
10.) Company uſed ill in ye Voyadge.
11   Spotting of his face & counter-
fetting sicknes.
12   The E. of Eſſex.

————————

Laſtly, he deſired ye company
to ioyne with him in prayer. &c.

[*Brit. Mus. Add.* MSS. 6789.]

Every paragraph of the speech is noted, but

not quite in the order of the speech as variously reported by those who witnessed the execution and heard it.   Circumstances occurred after Sir Walter began to speak, which may have caused the slight change in the order as here set down. This argues in favor of its being a note prepared beforehand.   If so it must have been written shortly before the speech, because the order for the execution was not given in the King's Bench Court till the afternoon of the 28th, and the execution was fixed for early the next morning.

There is a little confusion of the tenses, but this is not strange considering that the note was penned by a third person.   The last two lines, below the number 12, may have been added by Hariot afterwards, as they are in the past tense and third person, and are separated from the rest of the note by a dash.   This point is not numbered. It is possible that the first five lines were also added subsequently, as they are not numbered, and are placed near the top of the paper, as if interpolated, but they are in the same handwriting, and apparently were written with the same pen and ink.

At all events, whether written by Hariot before or after the deed, it is a precious contemporary document, and is another proof, if any more be needed, of the genuineness of the reported dying speech, and, consequently, that the famous 'Spanish papers' recently reproduced are forgeries and false. It requires no great stretch of the imagination with this little messenger in hand to believe that the ingenious teacher and friend of his youth, and for nearly two score years the constant companion of his manhood, passed that dreadful night with Sir Walter in the Gate House at Westminster, and after ' dear Bess ' had taken her leave at midnight, penned out this note of remembrance for his friend's morning guidance, that nothing should be forgotten in case the ague returned, which he feared even more than death.

A little more than a month after the execution of his friend, Hariot is found in his observatory at Sion taking observations of the comet of December 1618. His valuable observations are preserved among his mathematical papers. Du-

ring the eleven years following his primitive observations of the ' Hariot' comet of 1607, first at
Ilfracombe and later at Kidwely, great advances
had been made in the science of astronomy, chiefly
in consequence of the invention of the telescope,
and the discoveries by means of it. No mathematician in Europe was probably further advanced in this science than Hariot.

What particular discoveries belonged to him
and what to Galileo, Kepler and other contemporaries, it is very difficult to determine, since it
is now positively known that from 1609 or 1610
Hariot was a manufacturer and dealer in lenses,
or perspective glasses, as well as in perspective
trunks or telescopes; and that he was in correspondence with Kepler, and probably with
Galileo. He was easily the chief of astronomers
in England, and is known to have possessed the
earliest books of Galileo and to have sent them
to his disciples, Lower and Protheroe, in Wales.
Respecting this comet of 1618, he was in correspondence with Allen and Standish of Oxford
and other scholars at home and abroad.

In 'Certain Elegant Poems, Written By Dr. [Richard] Corbet, Bishop of Norwich. R. Cotes for Andrew Crooke, 1647,' 16°. The mirth-loving Bishop, in 'A Letter ſent from Doƈtor Corbet to Maſter [Sir Thomas] Ailebury, Decem. 9. 1618' [on the Comet of that year] is the following allusion to Hariot:

> *Burton* to *Gunter* Cants, and *Burton* heares
> From *Gunter*, and th' Exchange both tongue & eares
> By carriage : thus doth mired *Guy* complaine,
> His Waggon on their letters beares *Charles* Waine,
> *Charles* Waine, to which they ſay the tayle will reach
> And at this diſtance they both heare, and teach.
> Now for the peace of God and men, adviſe
> (Thou that haſt wherewithall to make us wiſe)
> Thine owne rich ſtudies, and deepe Harriots mine,
> In which there is no droſſe, but all refine,
> O tell us what to trust to, leſt we wax
> All ſtiffe and ſtupid with his paralex ;
> Say, ſhall the old Philoſophy be true ?
> Or doth he ride above the Moone think you? *etc.*

After the departure of the 'Blazing Starr' of December 1618, very little is known of Hariot, except that he lived at Sion while his patron the Earl was still in the Tower, where he was probably frequently visited by his man of science. The following letter, dated the 19th of January

1619, to him at Sion from Sir Thomas Aylesbury is interesting as showing the great interest
taken in his old master by his ' loytering scholar.' Many other letters of this stamp, breath-
ing love and ardent friendship, are found among
the Hariot papers, from Sir William Lower, Sir
John Protheroe, Sir Ferdinando Gorges, Dr Turner, and Sir Thomas Aylesbury. Here is a
sample :

> Sᵣ, Though I have bene yet soe little a while att New Mar-
> kett, that I have not any thing of moment to ympart; yet I
> thinke it not amisse to write a bare salutacoп̃s, and let yoᵘ know,
> that in theise wearie journeys I am often times comforted wᵗ the
> remembraunce of yoʳ kind love and paynes bestowed on yoʳ loy-
> tering scholar, whose little credit in the way of learning is all-
> waies underpropped wᵗ the name of soe worthie a Maister.
>
> The Comet being spent, the talke of it still runnes current here;
> The Kings mᵃ before my cumming spake wᵗ one of Cambridge
> called Olarentia, (a name able to beget beleefe of some extraor-
> dinarie qualities) but what satisfaction he gave, I cannot yet
> learne; here are papers out of Spayne about it, yea and frõ Roome,
> wᶜ I will endevoʳ to gett, and meane yᵗ yoᵘ shall partake of the
> newes as tyme serves.
>
> Cura ut valeas et me ames, who am ever trulie and unfaynedly
> yoᵣˢ att Commaund.   Tʜᴏ: Aʏʟᴇꜱʙᴜʀɪᴇ.

Olorén
Shaw
Mʳ Booth.

Newmarkett. 19, Jan. $\frac{1618}{1619}$.

Addressed: To my right woorthie frend
Mʳ. Tʜᴏᴍᴀꜱ Hᴀʀɪᴏᴛ
att Syon, theise, frõ Newmarkett.

Seal
of
Arms.

Between 1615 and 1620 there are evidences
of Hariot's failing health. He was greatly
troubled with a cancerous ulcer on the lip. How
early this began is not apparent. In 1610 his
friend Lower cautions him to be careful of his
health. There is in the British Museum among
the Hariot papers the drafts of three beautiful
letters in Latin written from Sion in 1615 and
1616 to a friend of distinction, name not mentioned, who had been recently appointed to some
medical office at court, in which he describes himself and his disease.

These letters show great resignation and Christian fortitude. He seemed to be getting better
in 1616, and expressed himself as somewhat
hopeful. The progress of the cancer and other
troubles cannot now probably be traced, but he
is found in the summer of 1621 lodging with his
old friend Thomas Buckner, in Threadneedle
Street, near the Royal Exchange, in the parish
of St Christopher. Buckner had been one of
Raleigh's ' First Colonie ' to Virginia in 1585
with Hariot, and Hariot, now in 1621, had come

s

up from Sion probably for medical advice near
the hospital. On the 29th of June he made or
executed his Will, and died three days after at
Buckner's, on the 2nd of July 1621. He was
buried the next day, according to the wish expressed in his will, in the old parish church of
St Christopher in Threadneedle Street.

Sifte viator, leviter preme,
Iacet hîc juxta, Quod mortale fuit,
C. V.
Thomæ Harrioti.
Hic fuit Doctiffimus ille Harriotus
de Syon ad Flumen Thamefin,
Patria & educatione
Oxonienfis,
Qui omnes fcientias Caluit,
Qui in omnibus excelluit,
Mathematicis, Philofophicis, Theologicis.
Veritatis indagator ftudiofiffimus,
Dei Trini-unius cultor piiffimus,
Sexagenarius, aut eo circiter,
Mortalitati valedixit, Non vitæ,
Anno Christi M.DC.XXI. Iulii 2.

Shortly after there was erected to his memory
in the chancel, at the expense, it is understood,
of his noble friend the Earl of Northumberland,
a fine marble monument, bearing the above neat
and appropriate inscription.

St Christopher's, a very old church, with its records (still preserved) extending back in an almost unbroken series to 1488, passed through many vicissitudes before it was finally swallowed up by the leviathan of the world's commerce. The site of it is now occupied by the south-west corner of the Bank of England on Princes Street, to the left of the entrance, nearly opposite the Mansion House. The church was restored and redecorated the year of Hariot's death, and again twelve years later, but was burnt in the great fire of 1666. Hariot's monument perished with it, but the inscription had been preserved by Stow. The church was rebuilt on the same foundation by Sir Christopher Wren in 1680.

About a century ago the church, with the whole parish of St Christopher (called then St Christopher-le-stocks because near the stocks standing at the east end of Cheapside), together with a large portion of two other parishes, St Margaret's and St Bartholomew's, was purchased by the Old Lady of Threadneedle Street for the site of the new Bank of England. Thus one great bank of this modern metropolis covers a large part of three parishes of old London.

The whole area of the Bank, however, was not given up to mammon, though still here men most do congregate, and worshippers most do worship.   One small consecrated spot, enough perhaps to leaven and memorize the whole site, was respected, and not built over.   It was the churchyard of St Christopher.   This ‘ God’s acre ’ the architect and the governors have dedicated to Beauty, Art, and Nature.   The little ‘ Garden of the Bank of England,’ the loveliest spot in all London at this day, measuring about twenty-four by thirty-two yards, was just a hundred years ago the little churchyard of St Christopher, where still repose the bones of THOMAS HARIOT.

Virginia, which once comprehended the present United States from South to North, has been called the monument to Sir Walter Raleigh.   So the Bank of England, built round the churchyard of St Christopher, may be called the monument to Thomas Hariot.

The present year, 1879, is just three centuries since Hariot went forth, a youth of twenty, from the University of Oxford. We have briefly told his story. England is all the richer for his life, and the world itself acknowledges the wealth of his science and the worth of his philosophy. The Bank of England is built round his bones, but it cannot cover his memory.

Stay, traveller, tread lightly ;
Near this spot lies what was mortal
of that most celebrated man
THOMAS HARRIOT.
He was the very learned Harriot
of Sion on Thames ;
by birth and education
an Oxonian,
Who cultivated all the sciences,
and excelled in all,
In Mathematics, Natural Philosophy, Theology.
A most studious investigator of truth,
A most pious worshipper of the Triune God,
At the age of sixty, or thereabouts,
He bade farewell to mortality, not to life,
July 2d A.D. 1621.

He lived, died, and was forgotten in the parish of St Christopher. Henceforward, whenever Englishmen and Americans, merchants and scholars, rich and poor, men of genius and men of money, enter this little 'Garden,' let them read there in English what Henry Percy originally set up in Latin, the above inscription.

An impression has gone abroad, traceable chiefly to Aubrey and to Anthony à Wood, that Hariot was unsound in religious principles and matters of belief ; that he was, in fact, not only a Deist himself, but that he exerted a baleful influence over Raleigh and his History as well as over the Earl of Northumberland. Not to misstate this utterly unfounded imputation, the very words of Wood, as first printed in his Athenae in 1691, and never since modified, are here given in full : ' But notwithstanding his great skill in mathematics, he had strange thoughts of the scripture, and always undervalued the old story of the creation of the world, and could never believe that trite position, *Ex nihilo nihil fit*. He made a *Philosophical Theology*, wherein he cast off the OLD TESTAMENT, so that consequently the NEW would have no foundation. He was a Deist, and his doctrine he did impart to the said Count [the Earl] and to Sir Walt. Raleigh when he was compiling the *History of the World*, and would controvert the matter with eminent divines of those times; who therefore having no good opinion of him, did look on the manner of his death as a judgment upon him for those matters, and for nullifying the scripture.'

It is needless to say that in all our investigations into the life, actions, and character of this eminent philosopher and Christian, from the time when, as a young man in 1585, he took delight in reading the Bible to the Indians of Virginia, down to the time that he made his remarkable will in 1621, not one word has been found in corroboration of these statements; but, on the contrary, many passages have appeared to contradict and disprove them. Let any one notice the numerous citations of the various books of the Bible in Raleigh's History, and he will surely fail to discover any evidence of Raleigh's being a Deist, or that Hariot had taught him to undervalue the scripture.

It is not necessary here to say more in this connection than to quote the following passage from one of the Latin letters in 1616 referred to above by Hariot to the eminent physician who had just received a high medical appointment at Court, describing himself and his terrible affliction [a cancer on the lip]. The passage is given in English, but the original Latin may be seen in the British Museum (Add. 6789). It seems to have been written on purpose to refute such slanders. He writes:

> Think of me as your sincere friend. Your interests are involved as well as mine. My recovery will be your triumph, but through the Almighty who is the Author of all good things. As I have now and then said, I believe these three points. I believe in God Almighty; I believe that Medicine was ordained by him; I trust the Physician as his minister. My faith is sure, my hope firm. I wait however with patience for everything in its own time according to His Providence. We must act earnestly, fight boldly, but in His name, and we shall conquer. Sic transit gloria mundi, omnia transibunt, nos ibimus, ibitis, ibunt. So passes away the glory of this world, all things shall pass away, we shall pass away, you will pass away, they will pass away.

There is unfortunately no portrait known of Hariot, and we can form no idea of his personal appearance; but, fortunately, the drafts of the three Latin letters to his eminent friend at Court, alluded to above, fully describe his terrible disease and other bodily infirmities in 1615 and 1616, and give us some notion of himself and his personal habits. His regular physician was Dr Turner, and his apothecary Mr Mayorne, both employed also by Sir Walter.

Dr Alexander Read, in his 'Chirurgicall Lectures of Tumors and Vlcers Delivered in the Chirurgeans Hall, 1632-34. London. 1638,' 4°, says in Treatise 2, Lecture 26, page 307 :

Cancerous ulcers also feize upon this part [lips]. This grief haftened the end of that famous Mathematician, Mr. Hariot, with whom I was acquainted but a fhort time before his death : whom at one time, together with Mr. Hughes, who wrote of the Globes, Mr. Warner, and Mr. Turperley, the Noble Earl of Northumberland, the favourer of all good learning, and Mecænas of learned men, maintained while he was in the Tower for their worth and various literature.

A great deal of misconception has hitherto prevailed respecting Hariot's great printed work on Algebra. His reputation as a mathematician has been permitted to hinge chiefly upon it, very much to his disadvantage. A brief bibliographical statement of facts will probably present the matter in a new light. But first let the book be described as it lies before us and has been described by many others since the days of

t

Professor Wallis, nearly two hundred years ago.

The Title is as follows : ' Artis Analyticae /
Praxis / Ad æquationes Algebraicas nouâ, ex-
peditâ, & generali / methodo, refoluendas : /
Tractatus / E pofthumis Thomæ Harrioti
Philofophi ac Mathematici ce- / leberrimi fche-
diafmatis fummâ fide & diligentiâ / defcriptus :/
Et/Jllvstrissimo Domino/Dom. HenricoPercio,/
Northvmbriæ Comiti,/Qui hæc primò, fub Pa-
tronatus & Munificentiæ fuæ aufpicijs / ad pro-
prios vfus elucubrata, in communem Mathema-
ticorum / vtilitatem, denuò reuifenda, defcri-
benda, & publicanda / mandauit, meritiffimi
Honoris ergò / Nuncupatus. / Londini / Apud
Robertvm Barker, Typographum / Regium :
Et Hæred. Io. Billii. / Anno 1631. / *Title, reverse blank* ; Prefatio 4 pages ; Text 180 pages,
and Errata 1 page (Bbb) followed by a blank
page, folio. A very handsomely printed book.
In the British Museum, 529 m 8, is Charles the
First's copy in old calf, gilt edges, with the royal
arms on the sides.   In the Preface the editors
(Aylesbury and Prothero aided by Warner) say :

Artis Analyticæ, cuius caufa hîc agitur, poft eruditum illud Græcorum fæculum antiquitatæ iamdiù & incultæ iacentis, reftitutionem *Francifcus Vieta*, Gallus, vir clariffimus, & ob infignem in fcientijs Mathematicis peritiam, Gallicæ gentis decus, primus fingulari confilio & intentato antehâc conamine aggreffus eft; atque ingenuam hanc animi fui intentionem per varios tractatus, quos in argumenti huius elaboratione eleganter & acutè confcripfit, pofteris teftatem reliquit. Dùm verò ille veteris Analytices reftitutionem, quam fibi propofuit, feriò molitus eft, non tàm eam reftitutam, quàm proprijs inuentioni-bus actam & exornatam, tanquàm nouam & fuam, nobis tradi-diffe videtur. Quod generali conceptu enuntiatum paulò fufiùs explicandum eft ; vt, oftenfo eo quod primùm à *Vieta* in infti-tuto fuo promouendo actum eft, quid pofteà ab authore noftro doctiffimo *Thomâ Harrioto*, qui illum certamine ifto Analytico fequntus eft, praeftitum fit, meliùs innotefcere poffit. [Which done into English is substantially as follows]

Francis Vieta, a Frenchman, a most distinguished man, and on account of his remarkable skill in Mathematical Science the honour of the French nation, first of all with singular genius and with industry hitherto unattempted undertook the restora-tion of the analytic art, of which subject we are here treating, which after the learned age of the Greeks for a long time had become antiquated and remained uncultivated : and by various treatises which he eloquently and ingeniously wrote in the working out of this line of argument, left a record to posterity of this noble design of his mind. But while he seriously la-boured at the restoration of the old Analysis, which he had proposed to himself, he seems not so much to have transmitted to us a restoration of that science, as a new and original method, worked out and illustrated by his own discoveries. This, having been enunciated in general terms, must be explained a little more at length ; so that having shown what was first effected by Vieta in promoting his design, it may be more clear, what was afterwards performed by our very learned author

Thomas Harriot, who followed him in these analytical investigations.

And at the end of the volume, on page 180, is the following explanatory note :

AD MATHEMATICES STUDIOSOS.

'Ex omnibus *Thomæ Harrioti* fcriptis Mathematicis, quòd opus hoc Analyticum primum in publicum emiſſum ſit, haud inconfultò factum eſt. Nam, quùm reliqua eius opera, multiplici inuentorum nouitate excellentia, eodem omninò quo tractatus iſte (Logiſtices ſpeciofæ exemplis omnimodis totus compofitus) ſtilo Logiſtico, hactenùs inuſitato, confcripta ſint, eâ certè ratione ſit, vt prodromus hic tractatus, vltra proprium ipſius inæſtimabilem vſum, reliquis *Harrioti* fcriptis, de quorum editione iam ſeriò cogitatur, pro neceſſario prǫparamento ſiue introductorio opportunè inferuire poſſit. De quâ quidem acceſſoriâ operis huius vtilitate rerum Mathematicarum ſtudiofos paucis his præmonuiſſe operæprecium eſſe duximus.' [Which being interpreted reads as follows in English]

TO STUDENTS OF MATHEMATICS.

It is not without good reason that, of all Thomas Harriot's Mathematical writings, this on Analysis has been published first. For whereas all his remaining works, remarkable for their manifold novelties of discovery, are written precisely in the same, hitherto unusual, logical style as this treatise (which consists entirely of varied specimens of beautiful reasoning); this was certainly done that this preliminary treatise, besides its own inestimable utility, might suitably serve as a necessary preparation or introduction to the study of Harriot's remaining works, the publication of which is now under serious consideration. Of this accessory use of this treatise we have thought it worth while to remind mathematical students in these brief remarks.

From this it appears that Hariot's system of Analytics or Algebra was based on that of his friend and correspondent François Vieta, as Vieta's was avowedly based on that of the ancients. There appears to have been no attempt whatever on the part of the Englishman to appropriate the honors of the Frenchman, as many foreign writers have charged. Full credit was given by Hariot and his friends to the distinguished French mathematician.

But Hariot's modifications, improvements, and simplifications were so distinct and marked that from the first, and long before publication, they were called among his students and correspondents ' Hariot's Method,' meaning thereby only Hariot's peculiarities, without reference to the great merits of Vieta's restoration, modification, adaptation, and improvement of the old analyses from the times of the Greeks.

Vieta's ' Canon Mathematicus' was published at Paris in 1579, and was reissued in London with a new title in 1589 as his ' Opera Mathematica.' But this work does not contain the

Algebra. That was first published in 1591 under the following title :

'Francisci Vietæ / In Artem Analyticam / Isagoge / Seorſim excuſſa ab Opere reſtitutæ Mathematicæ / Analyſeos, seu, Algebraicâ nouâ. / Tvronis, / Apud Iametivm Mettayer Typographium Regium. / Anno 1591.' / folio. A Supplement appeared in 1593. Seven years later there came out under the auspices of Ghetaldi, a young Italian nobleman of mathematical tastes, who had been studying in Paris, the following :—' De Nvmerosa Potestatvm / Ad Exegeſum / Resolvtione. / Ex Opere reſtitutæ Mathematicæ Analyſeos, / ſeu, Algebrâ nouâ / Francisci Vietæ. / Parisiis, / Excudebat David le Clerc. / 1600.' / folio. On the last page of this book is an interesting letter from Marino Ghetaldi to his preceptor Michele Coignetto, dated at Paris the 15th of February 1600.

These three thin folio volumes of great rarity are models of typographic beauty. They manifestly served as the model for printing Hariot's Algebra in 1631. The set here described (the three bound in one volume), Prince Henry's own copies, bearing his arms and the Prince of Wales' feathers, is preserved in the British Museum, press-marked 530, m. 10.

Thus Vieta's method appears to have been given to the world in three instalments between 1591 and 1600, while the author himself died in 1603. It was probably in reference to one or both of these works that Lower gently reproached Hariot for having allowed himself to be anticipated in the public announcement of his discoveries in Algebra by Vieta. It has already been seen, on page 101 above, what Torperley, the friend of Vieta, wrote of his two masters in 1602, and also, on page 121, what Lower wrote to Hariot in 1610.

One is forced, therefore, to the conclusion that by 1600, if not some time before, Hariot had completed his method in Algebra, and distributed his well known problems to his admiring scholars. It has also been seen how, from 1603 to the day of his death, he was occupied in many other absorbing matters connected with

Raleigh and Percy. Yet he may have felt, as Lower expressed it, that when he surveyed his storehouse of inventions this one of Algebra might seem in 'comparison of manie others smal or of no value.' The matter is introduced here mainly because certain foreign writers, rebutting Wallis's patriotic claims in behalf of Hariot, have not only accused Hariot of appropriating Vieta's rights, but they even describe the distinguished English mathematician as working on the 'Cartesian Method.' While the truth appears to be that Hariot's method in Algebra, though not published for more than thirty years after its invention, must date from a time when Descartes was scarcely four years old.

On the other hand, on looking into Descartes' great and original work on geometry, first published in 1637, six years after Hariot's Algebra first saw the light in print, one is not disposed to accuse the great philosopher of plagiarism because in working out his problems of great novelty in reference to geometrical curves he employed any systems of notation and calculation in algebra (Hariot's among the others) that happened to be before the world. The point or essence of Descartes' work was geometry and not algebra. Therefore, in climbing to his loft, he was perfectly justified in using the ladder which Hariot had left, as it was then in general use, and was only an incidental aid in his independent calculations, especially as the fame of his great mathematical brother was well established, and he had been already sixteen years in St Christopher's. Vieta therefore had manifestly no just reason to complain, and Descartes stands acquitted.

The history of Hariot's *Praxis* has attracted a great deal of attention for more than two centuries and has long been obscured by many misconceptions and erroneous statements. In the first place it has been always said from the days of Collins that it was edited by Walter Warner, and Wood adds that Warner was to have his pension continued by Algernon Percy, for that scientific labor. There is evidence that Warner, though employed on the work by Sir Thomas

u

Aylesbury, was not the sole editor. See Aylesbury's Letter to the Earl on page 189.

The book led to a great deal of international or patriotic controversy, and with great injustice to Hariot was treated by the English advocates as his masterpiece in science. Wallis in 1685 in his History of Algebra, after much correspondence with Collins and others on the subject between 1667 and 1676, became Hariot's English champion. The controversy respecting the Methods of Hariot and of Descartes became as warm as that respecting the discoveries of Leibnitz and of Newton.

Wallis ranked Oughtred's *Clavis* and Hariot's *Praxis* very high, and because both were first printed in 1631, treated them as productions or inventions of that year, whereas Hariot's method, as we have seen, had been long practically before his disciples ; and was, ten years after the author's death, given to the world avowedly as an 'accessory' only, or preliminary treatise, that it 'might suitably serve as a necessary preparation or introduction to the study of Hariot's remaining works, the publication of which is now under serious consideration.' Unfortunately this excellent scheme fell through, probably in consequence of the death of the Earl of Northumberland, and perhaps partly because of the death of Nathaniel Torporley who had long been engaged in 'penning the doctrine' of Hariot's mathematical papers. They both died in 1632, shortly after the publication of the Praxis. Wallis's charge had a basis of truth, but it was narrow and petty. As an Algebraist he seems to have lost sight of the main point, that Descartes' great work was on Geometry and not on Algebra, and that Hariot's method, though first printed in 1631, was almost as old as Descartes himself.

Montucla the French mathematician, near the close of the last century, in his History of Mathematics, summed up the controversy raised by Wallis including the minor one raised by Dr Zach in 1785, clearing Descartes of Wallis's charges and relegating Hariot to the respectability of a second-rate mathematician. If Montucla's verdict be based on mathematical reason-

ing as loose and slipshod as is his statement of
the historical points of the case, to say nothing
of his utter ignorance of Hariot's biography and
true position as an English man of science, one
feels justified in rejecting it as worthless : as one
also is compelled to do the vapid conclusions
drawn from Montucla which have since found
their way into many recent biographical dictionaries and into many pretentious articles in learned
encyclopædias respecting Hariot and his works.

The truth seems to be that Hariot was un-
lucky and fell into oblivion accidentally.   He
was a man of immense industry and great men-
tal power, but perhaps careless of his scientific
and literary reputation.   As has been seen, he
always had many irons in the fire, and was overtaken by death in the prime of life, leaving, as
his will shows, many things unfinished, and none
of his papers in a state ready for publication.
He was surrounded by the best of friends, but
time and opportunity, as so often happens in the
affairs of busy men, worked against him, and he
was well nigh consigned to forgetfulness.

However, after a half century's slumber, when the great fire of London had destroyed his monument, and too late many scholars were minded to attempt the recovery and preservation of memorials of the past, John Collins the mathematician began soundings in the pool of oblivion for Hariot and his papers. He and his correspondents fished up a great deal of truth and history, but so mixed with error and conjecture that the results, though interesting, are misleading.

In the 'Correspondence of Scientific Men of the Seventeenth Century, Edited by Professor S. J. Rigaud, 2 volumes, Oxford 1841,' 8°, are found the following instructive and amusing passages :

As for Geysius, he published an Algebra and Stereometria divers years before the first edition of the Clavis [of Oughtred, 1631] was extant in Mr. Harriot's method, out of which Alsted took what he published of algebra in his Encylopædia printed in 1630, the year before the Clavis was first extant (see Christmannus and Raymarus). Mr. Harriot's method is now more used than Oughtred's, and himself in the esteem of Dr. Wallis not beneath Des Cartes. Dr. Hakewill, in his Apology, tells you Harriot was the first that squared the area of a spherical triangle; and I can tell you, by the perusal of some papers of Torporley's it appears that Harriot could make the sign of any arch at demand, and the converse, and apply a

table of sines to solve all equations, and treated largely of
figurate arithmetic.   His papers fell into the hands of Sir
Thomas Aylesbury, father to the Lord Chancellor's lady, where
I hope they still are, unless they had the hard fate to be lent
out, before the fire, and be burned, as some have said.

Collins to Wallis, no date, circa 1670, vol. ii, page 478.

As to Harriot, he was so learned, saith Dr. Pell, that had
he published all he knew in algebra, he would have left little
of the chief mysteries of that art unhandled.   His papers fell
into the hands of Sir Thomas Aylesbury, who was father to
the late Lord Chancellor's [Clarendon] Lady, by which means
they fell into the Lord Chancellor's hands, to whom application
was made by the members of the Royal Society to obtain them :
his lordship (then in the height of his dignity and employments)
gave order for a search to be made, and in result the answer was, they
could not be found.   I am afraid the search was but perfunctory,
and that, if his lordship (now at leisure) were solicited for
them, he might write to his son the Lord Cornbury to make
a diligent search for them.   One Mr. Protheroe, in Wales,
was executor to Mr. Harriot, and from him the Lord Vaughan,
the Earl of Carbery's son, received more than a quire of Mr.
Harriot's Analytics.   The Lord Brounker has about two sheets
of Harriot de Motu et Collisione Corporum, and more of his
I know not of : there is nothing of Harriot's extant but that
piece which Mons. Garibal hath.

Collins to Vernon, not dated but circa 1671, vol. i, page 153.

Upon this passage Professor Rigaud makes the following note, written at Oxford in 1841 :

Harriot's will is not to be found, but Camden says that
he left his property to Viscount Lisle and Sir Thomas Aylesbury.   Lord Lisle's share of the papers appear to have been
given up to his father-in-law, Henry earl of Northumberland,
who had been Harriot's munificent patron, and they descended

with the family property to the E. of Egremont, by whom a large portion has been given to the British Museum, and the remainder are still preserved at Petworth. Sir Thomas Aylesbury's share became the property of his son-in-law Lord Chancellor Clarendon, to whom the Royal Society applied, but, as it appears, without obtaining them. (See Birch, Hist. Royal Society, vol. ii, pp. 120, 126, 309.)—*Vol. i, page* 153.

Here seems to be the germ of Professor Wallis's charge of plagiarism against Descartes, written to Collins twelve years before it appeared in the first edition of his History of Algebra in English in 1685. It subsequently took a wider range, and was strenuously defended by Wallis when opposed:

That which I most valued in his [Des Cartes] method, and which pleased me best, was the way of bringing over the whole equations to one side, making it equal to nothing, and thereby forming his compound equations by the multiplication of simples, from thence also determining the number of roots, real or imaginary, in each. This artifice, on which all the rest of his doctrine is grounded, was that which most made me to set a value on him, presuming it had been properly his own; but afterwards I perceived that he had it from Hariot, whose Algebra was published after his death in the year 1631, six years before Des Cartes' Geometry in French in the year 1637 : and yet Des Cartes makes no mention at all of Harriot, whom he follows in designing his species by small letters, and the powers of them by the number of dimensions, without the characters of q, c, qq, &c.

Wallis to Collins, Oxford, 12 *April* 1673, *vol. ii, page* 573.

And had I but known of any precedent, (as since in Harriot I find one, and I think but one $\checkmark$ —*dddddd*,) I should not have scrupled to follow it; but I was then too young an algebraist to innovate without example. Since that time I have been more venturous, and I find now that others do not scruple to use it as well as I. [Just what Descartes did. He 'innovated' prior to 1637, when he took Hariot's well recognized notation in algebra to work out his problems in geometry for which Hariot himself would have thanked him.]

Wallis to Collins, May 6, 1673, vol. ii, page 578.

One Torporley, long since, left a manuscript treatise in Latin in Sion College, wherein is a much more copious table of figurate numbers, which I have caused to be transcribed, with what he says de combinationibus, to send to Mr. Strode.

On this passage, extracted from a letter from Collins to Baker, dated the 19th of August, 1676, Professor Rigaud has the following note, written in 1841, vol. ii, page 5 :

Nath. Torporley left his manuscripts to Sion College, where he spent the latter years of his life; but the greater part of them was destroyed by the fire of London. Reading, in his catalogue of the library, mentions only one, " Corrector Analyticus," which is an attack on Warner for the manner in which he had edited Harriot's " Artis Analyticæ Praxis." This is a short tract, and incomplete. There is, however, another volume, A. 37-39, entitled, "Algebraica, Tabulæ Sinuum, &c." in which Torporley's hand may be certainly recognized. Wood, in the list of his works, speaks of "Congestor opus Mathematicam,— imperfect." A perfect copy of this treatise is in Lord Macclesfield's possession, and probably once belonged to Collins.

Perhaps the best comment that one can make on the wild and extraordinary statements contained in the above extracts is to ask the reader to read over Hariot's Will, given entire on pages 193-203, and especially this *Item* respecting his Mathematical and other Writings, and the Rev. Nathaniel Torporley, from which it will appear that all his valued papers were bequeathed with great care to the Earl of Northumberland, to be deposited in his library in a trunk with lock and key, after they had been looked over and perused, by Mr Torporley, and (the waste papers having been weeded out) the whole arranged by him 'to the end that *after hee doth vnderstand them* he may make use in penning such doctrine that belongs unto them for publique use.' This, of course, was to be done under the supervision of the four Executors, who were persons of no less distinction than Sir Robert Sidney Knight Viscount Lisle, John Protheroe Esquire, Thomas Aylesbury Esquire, and Thomas Buckner Mercer.

ITEM I ordayne and Constitute the aforesaid Nathaniel Thorperley first to be Overseer of my Mathematical Writings to be received of my Executors to peruse and order and to separate the

X

Chiefe of them from my waste papers, to the end that after hee doth vnderstand them hee may make use in penninge such doctrine that belongs vnto them for publique vses as it shall be thought Convenient by my Executors and him selfe. And if it happen that some manner of Notacions or writings of the said papers shall not be understood by him then my desire is that it will please him to confer with Mr Warner or Mr Hughes Attendants on the afore said Earle Concerning the aforesaid doubte. And if hee be not resolued by either of them That then hee Conferre with the aforesaid John Protheroe Esquier or the aforesaid Thomas Alesbury Esquior. (I hopeing that some or other of the aforesaid fower last nominated can resolve him). And when hee hath had the use of the said papers soe longe as my Executors and hee have agreed for the use afore said That then he deliver them againe unto my Executors to be putt into a Convenient Truncke with a locke and key and to be placed in my Lord of Northumberlandes Library and the key thereof to be delivered into his Lordshipps hands. And if at anie tyme after my Executors or the afore said Nathaniell Thorperley shall agayne desire the use of some or all of the said Mathematicall papers That then it will please the said Earle to lett anie of the aforesaid to have them for theire use soe long as shall be thought Convenient, and afterwards to be restored agayne unto the Truncke in the afore said Earles Library. Secondly my will and desire is that the said Nathaniell Thorperley be alsoe Overseere of other written bookes and papers as my Executors and hee shall thincke Convenient.

This will, of extraordinary interest, has fallen to our lot to exhume, after many antiquaries and scholars had long sought it in vain. It was recently discovered in the Archdeaconry Court of London, just the place where one would least expect to find it. One has only to read the document to read the character of the man—good, learned, affectionate, charitable and just. He was carried off by a terrible disease, away from home, but among friends. He left his affairs and fame in loving hands. His will was proved on the 4th day after his death by two of the Executors, Sir Thomas Aylesbury and Mr Buckner, with the right reserved to the other two to act subsequently. It is found by papers in the British Museum that Sir John Protheroe did act, for there is a very long list of manuscripts, copied from Protheroe's list of papers delivered to Mr Torporley, which served as a receipt for them, and which was returned with the papers.

Mr Torporley then, it is manifest, had in hand the papers and returned them, but it is not apparent what amount of labor he bestowed upon them. They do not appear to be properly arranged, nor have the waste papers been weeded out. From Protheroe's list and other circumstances it is likely that nothing has been destroyed, except perhaps the Raleigh accounts and the Irish papers in the ' canvas baggs.' The papers were at Sion, and were placed in a trunk and delivered to the Earl, who left the Tower only sixteen days after Hariot's death. They subsequently found their way to Petworth, another seat of the Earl, where the trunk and half of the papers still remain, in the possession of the Earl of Leconsfield, a branch of the Northumberland family. They are briefly described in this manner by Mr Alfred J. Horwood in the Sixth Report of the Historical Manuscript Commission for 1877, page 319, folio.

A black leather box containing several hundred leaves of figures and calculations by Hariot.

A large bundle of Hariot's papers. They are arranged in packets by Professor Rigaud. Spots on the Sun. Comets of 1607 and 1618. The Moon. Jupiter's Satellites. Projectiles, Centre of Gravity, Reflection of bodies. Triangles. Snell's Eratosthenes Batavus. Geometry. Calendar. Conic Sections. De Stella Martis. Drawings of Constellations, papers on Chemistry and Miscellaneous Calculations. Collections from Observations of Hannelius, Warner, Copernicus, Tycho Brahe. On the vernal and autumnal equinoxes, the solstices, orbit of the Earth, length of the year, &c. Algebra.

A similar collection, but not yet arranged, catalogued, numbered or bound, is carefully preserved in the Manuscript Department of the

British Museum (Additional, 6782-6789), in eight thick Solander cases, probably as much in bulk as the Petworth papers. They were presented to the Museum by the Earl of Egremont in 1810. Why the two collections were separated does not appear. The Museum papers contain much that is waste, but much also that is of importance equal probably to those at Petworth.

Mr Torporley was in effect appointed by Hariot his literary and scientific editor under the direction of the Executors. No papers were left ready for publication. It must have required great study and labor to master them sufficiently to pen for public use such doctrine or science as belonged to them. Torporley lived in Shropshire, but a few years after Hariot's death he retired from his rectorship and removed to London, taking rooms in 1630 at Sion College in London Wall, when that institution was first founded. It contained then as now a library for the use of the Clergy, and a few suites of apartments for those who desired to reside on the premises. It never was a College or place of instruction, but a sort of guild or Clergyman's Club. At this time Mr Torporley was about seventy years old. He died in his chambers at Sion College in April 1632, and was buried on the 17th of that month in the Church of St Alphage, close by. In a nuncupative will spoken the 14th of April, a copy of which is before the writer, he left his books and manuscripts to the Sion College Library. A complete list of about 170 books and several manuscripts is preserved in the 'Donors' Book.' A few of the books are said to have been destroyed by the fire of London, but probably none of the manuscripts were lost.

Torporley's manuscripts, as has been stated, have often been referred to, and sometimes copied, but their true history and character is explained by Hariot's Will. There are really but two manuscripts relating to Hariot. The more important one comprises 116 closely-written folio leaves, or 232 pages, all in Torporley's handwriting. It bears no title or designation. Hence various writers who have seen it, from Collins, Wood, and Dr Zach, have given it different names, such as, '*Ephemeris Chysometria*,' ' *Congestor opus Mathematicum*,' etc. but it appears to be nothing more nor less than Torporley's attempt to pen out such doctrine as he found in Hariot's papers. The leaves are numbered, 1 to 16 containing a Treatise on Hariot's Theory of Numbers. Leaves 17 to 25 are tables of the divisors of odd numbers up to 20,300. On the verso of leaf 25 the Theory of Numbers is resumed, extending to the recto of 27. On the verso of leaf 27 begins the treatise on the properties of Triangles and ends on leaf 34. Leaves 35 to 55 comprise examples of Algebraical processes, and leaves 56 to 116 contain Tables (probably tabulæ sinuum?) up to 180°. On the second leaf the Author speaks of himself as working out, or working on Hariot's principles, and also as making use of the writings of Vieta. He adds:

'And since it is our principal design to explain the improvement in this science [the Properties of Numbers and Triangles] discovered by our friend Thomas Hariot; but he neither completely reformed it (which indeed was not necessary) nor gave a full account of it, but only strengthened it where it was defective, and by treating in his own way the points of the science which were heretofore more difficult, rendered them clear and easy.'

This manuscript was probably intended for another printed volume of Hariot's mathematical works, but owing to the deaths about the same time, 1632, of the venerable editor and the noble patron this work never bore a definite name and never saw the light of the press.

CORRECTOR ANALYTICUS
Artis poſthumæ
THOMÆ HARIOTI
Vt Mathematici eximij, perrarò
Vt Philoſophi Audentes, frequentius } errantis
Vt Hominis evanidi, inſigniter
Ad
Fidedigniorem refutationem Philopſeudoſophiæ
Atomiſticæ, per eum Reducis, et præ
cæteris eius Portentis
ſeriò
corripiendæ, anathematyzandæq̃
Compendiũ Antimonitorũ, et Speciminale
exanthorati iã Senioris
Na : Torporley.
Vt
Noverit Arbiter
Caveat Emptor.
non bene Ripæ
Creditur, ipſe Aries etiam nunc Vellera ſiccat.
[*Virgil*, Ecl. III. 94, 95.]

This Second Manuscript is a pretentious but small affair. It was manifestly written at Sion

College after the *Praxis* appeared in 1631. It is only the preface or the opening of a growl of envy or disappointment. It shows clearly that Torporley himself was not the editor of the Algebra or Praxis. The above is the pedantic title-page, given line for line and verbatim.

The manuscript is in small quarto, and exclusive of the title (which, indeed, is the nub of the achievement) contains only nine pages, breaking off abruptly in the middle of a sentence. He criticises the editors of Hariot's Algebra, the executors Aylesbury and Protheroe, aided by Warner, who were all eminent mathematicians. He speaks of the administrators or editors as if more than one, and does not mention Warner, or lead us to believe that he was sole editor. Only a small portion of this projected criticism seems ever to have been written. It appears to have been begun in senile peevishness, containing only a few prefatory remarks and discussing some algebraical questions with the fancied errors of the editors. No mention is made of the 'Atomic Theory,' as promised

y

on the title-page, which is here done into English, and is as follows :—

THE ANALYTICAL CORRECTOR
of the posthumous scientific writings
of THOMAS HARRIOT.

As an excellent Mathematician one who very seldom ⎫
As a bold Philosopher one who occasionally   ⎬ erred,
As a frail Man one who notably   ⎭
For
the more trustworthy refutation of the pseudo-philosophic
atomic theory, revived by him and, outside his
other strange notions, deserving of
reprehension and anathema.
A Compendious Warning with specimens by the aged
and retired-from-active-life
Na: Torporley.
So that
The critic may know
The buyer may beware.
It is not safe to trust to the bank,
The bell-wether himself is drying his fleece.

The 'Corrector Analyticus' may be found printed in full (but without the quaint titles) in 'The Historical Society of Science. A Collection of Letters illustrative of Science, edited by J. O. Halliwell,' London, 1841, 8°, Appendix, pages 109-116. For Torporley's curious paper entitled ' A Synopsis of the Controversie of Atoms,' see Brit. Mus. Mss, Birch 4458, 2.

Mr Torporley informs us, and the papers appear to bear him out in the statement, that Hariot wrote memoranda, problems, etc. on loose pieces of paper, and then arranged them in sets fastened together according to the subjects treated of. He adds, 'First then let me speak of Hariot's method, of which frequent mention will have to be made in the following pages; so that the reader may understand why some things are stated and some passed over: here I cannot but complain, that I find it a serious defect that his Commentators have so completely transformed it [the Praxis] that they not only do not retain his order but not even his language.' Again he writes, 'But not even those well-thought-out and necessary to be known matters, which have been delivered to us, have been handed down to posterity by his administrators with the fidelity and accuracy promised.' The suspicion is raised that Torporley's age and dilatoriness compelled the accomplished executors to take the editorial matter in hand themselves and hinc illæ lacrymæ.

On the back of the above title-page is another attempt of the same sort as follows, showing that this deed of pedantry was committed at Sion College :

CORRECTOR
sive
Notæ in Analyticam
Novam, Novatam, Posthumā
quatenus
Fallacem, Defectivam, Extrariam
cum
Apodictica refutatione Atomorum
Somnij, præ cæteris Novatorum
portentis corripiendi Ana-
thematizandiq₃:
Ex Collegio Sion Londinenſi
perfuncti Senis Artemq₃ reponentis
N T
Extremũ hoc munus morientis
habetor :
Σκληρὸν πρὸς κέντρον λακτίζειν.
nec bene Ripae
Creditur ipse Aries etiã nunc Vellera ſiccat.

There are one or two unimportant papers a-mong the Torperley manuscripts that bear marks of having belonged to the Hariot papers, and there is a manuscript by Warner, entitled, ‘Certayne Definitions of the Planisphere.’ Any one curious in the history of Torperley may find in the Calendar of State Papers, Domestic Series, 1636, page 364, how his property was purloined by Mr Spencer, the first Librarian of Sion College. He was sued by Mistress Payne the administratrix and was compelled to disgorge £40 in money, eleven diamond rings, eight gold rings, two bracelets, etc. Then Archbishop Laud took away Spencer's librarianship, and let him drop.

Mr William Spence of Greenock published in Nov. 1814, a work entitled, ' Outlines of a Theory of Algebraical Equations deduced from the Principles of Harriott, and extended to the Fluxional or differential Calculus. By William Spence. London, for the Author, by Davis and Dickson, 1814, 8°, *iv and* 80 *pages*. Privately printed, intended ' exclusively for the perusal of those gentlemen to whom it is addressed.' He says in his prefatory note that—

' As the principles are drawn from that theory of equations, by which Harriott has so far advanced the science of algebra.' The author says, page 1, ' Until the publication of Harriot's *Artis Analyticæ Praxis*, no extended theory of equations was given. Harriot considered algebraical equations merely as analytical expressions, detached wholly from the operations by which they might be individually produced ; and, carrying all the terms over to one side, he assumed the hypothesis, that, as in that state the equation was equal to nothing, it could always be reduced to as many simple factors as there were units in the index of its highest power.'

Between 1606 and 1609 a very interesting and historically instructive correspondence took place between Kepler and Hariot upon several important scientific subjects. Five of the letters are given in full in ' Joannis Keppleri Aliorumque Epistolae Mutuae. [Frankfort] 1718,' folio, to which the reader is referred, but a brief abstract of them may not be out of place here. The letters are numbered from 222 to 226 and fill pages 373 to 382. The correspondence was begun by Kepler:

Letter 222, dated Prague, 11 October, 1606, from John Kepler to Thomas Hariot.

Kepler had heard of Hariot's acquirements in Natural Philosophy from his friend John Eriksen. Would be glad to know Hariot's views as to the origin and essential differences of colours; also on the question of refraction of rays of light; and the causes of the Rainbow ; and of haloes round the sun.

Letter 223, dated London, 11 December, 1606, from Thomas Hariot to John Kepler.

Had received with pleasure Kepler's letter ; but should not be able to answer it at length, being in indifferent health, so that it was not easy to write or even carefully to reflect. Sends a table of the results of experiments on equal bulks of various liquids and transparent solids (thirteen in number, including spring, rain, and salt water; Spanish and Rhenish wine; vinegar; spirits of wine; oils and glass). The angle of incidence is 30° in each case; also the specific gravity of each substance is given. Then he discusses the reason why refraction takes place. Promises to write on the Rainbow; but will merely say at present that it is to be explained by the reflection on the concave superficies and the refraction at the convex superficies of each separate drop.

Letter 224 is from John Kepler to Thomas Hariot, dated at Prague, 11 August, 1607.

Thanks Hariot for his table, which supplies matter for serious consideration. Asks questions as to how he defines the angles of incidence and refraction; and goes on to discuss the reasons of refraction. Agrees with Hariot as to his views about the Rainbow; but will be very glad to receive his treatises on Colours and the Rainbow.

Letter 225 is from Thomas Hariot to John Kepler, dated at Syon, near London, 13 July (o.s.), 1608.

The departure of Eriksen and other matters do not allow leisure to write at length. The turpentine (oleum terebinthinum) was not the same as that experimented on by Kepler but a purer and lighter article (Sp. grav. ·87). The angle of incidence is understood as defined by Alhazen and Vitellio [first published 1572]. Points out some errors in Vitellio's second table of refractions. As to the causes of refraction, Hariot believes in the theory of the vacuum; 'where we still stick in the mud'. Hopes God (Deum optimum maximum) will soon put an end to this. Wishes for Kepler's meteorological records for the last two years, and will send his own notes in return. Gilbert, author of a work on the magnet, had recently died, leaving in his brother's hands a book entitled 'De Globo et Mundo nostro sublunari Philosophia nova contra Peripateticos, lib. 5.' [A treatise, in five books, on Natural Philosophy, in answer to the Peripatetics.] The book is likely to be published before the end of the year. Hariot had read some chapters; and saw that Gilbert defends the doctrine of a vacuum. Not to leave a vacuum on this page (says Hariot), it is remarkable that though gold is both heavy and opaque, when beaten out into gold-leaf the light of a candle can be seen through it, though it appears of a green colour.

Letter 226, from John Kepler to Thomas Hariot, is dated from Prague, September, 1609.

Excuses himself for not having replied sooner; having been very busy; but would not lose the present opportunity of writing. Discusses the questions of refraction and the vacuum. Commentaries on Mars entitled 'Astronomia Nova αἰτιολόγητος or Physica Cœlestis,' have been published at Frankfort; has not a copy by him. Regrets to hear of the death of Gilbert. Hopes his work on Magnetism will also be published; and that Eriksen will bring a copy with him. Promises to send a copy of his own meteorological observations; and hopes to receive Hariot's.

These studies in optics and this correspondence with the learned Kepler indicate Hariot's great advancement in natural philosophy as early as 1606 to 1609 and give an earnest of his inventive genius and scientific enterprise with his telescope in the astronomical discoveries which immediately followed in 1609 to 1613. Before awarding all the prizes for discoveries and inventions in mathematics, philosophy and natural science to claimants throughout the wide Republic of Letters, let modest Hariot be heard and examined. Let his papers and all his credentials be laid out before the high court of science, not in the light of to-day, but contemporaneously with those of Tycho, Kepler, Galileo, Snell, Vieta and Descartes. Hariot himself has claimed nothing, but Justice and Historical Truth are bound to assign him a niche appropriate to his merits.

To show that Hariot, like his friends Hakluyt and Purchas, was alive to everything geographical as well as mathematical going on, the following is given from the original manuscript among the Hariot papers in the British Museum (Add. 6789):

Three reasons to prove that there is a passage from the Northwest into the South-sea.

1. The tydes in Port Nelson (where S^r. Tho : Button did winter, were constantly, 15, or, 18, foote ; w^c is not found in any Bay Throughout the world but in such seas as lie open att both ends to the mayne Ocean.

2. Every strong Westerne winde did bring into the Harbo^r where he wintered, soe much water, that the Neap-tydes were equall to the Spring-tydes, notw^{t}standing y^t the harbo^r was open only to ye E.N.E.

3. In comming out of the harbo^r, shaping his course directly North, about, 60, degrees, he found a stronge race of a tyde, setting due East and West, w^c in probabilitie could be noe other thing, than the tyde comming from the West, and retourning from the East.

Among the manuscripts in the handwriting of Hariot in the British Museum (Add. 6789) are these samples of ingenious trifling. No evidence is forthcoming that he was ever a married man, but that he occasionally let himself down from pure mathematics and high philosophy and amused himself with anagrams is plain enough. Here are a few specimens on his own name.

ANAGRAMS ON THOMAS HARIOTUS

Tu homo artis has	traho hosti mufa
Homo has vt artis	O trahit hos mufa
Homo hasta vtris	oh, os trahit mufa
vitus	oho trahit mifas
rutis	oho, trahis mutás
Humo astra hosti	oho, fum Charitas.

If the pertingent Reader still craves more evidence of the extent of Hariot's friendships, and the universality of his acquirements, let him read the following pithy, quaint, and beautiful tribute paid to him by blind Old Homer's Chapman in 1616. It is found in the Preface to the Reader in the first complete edition of Homer's works translated by George Chapman, London [1616], f°.

No cōference had with any one liuing in al the nouelties I prefume I haue found. Only fome one or two places I haue fhewed to my worthy and moft learned friend, M. Harriots, for

his cenfure how much mine owne weighed : whofe iudgement
and knowledge in all kinds, I know to be incomparable, and
bottomleffe ; yea, to be admired as much, as his moft blame-
les life, and the right facred expence of his time, is to be
honoured and reuerenced. Which affirmation of his cleare vn-
matchedneffe in all manner of learning ; I make in contempt
of that naftie objection often thruft vpon me ; that he that will
iudge, muft know more then he of whom he iudgeth ; for fo a
man fhould know neither God nor himfelf. Another right
learned, honeft, and entirely loued friend of mine, M. Robert
Hews, I muft needs put into my confest conference touching
Homer, though very little more than that I had with M. Harriots. Which two, I proteft, are all, and preferred to all.

It remains to say two words more about Baron
Zach's ' discovery' of the Hariot papers at Petworth in 1784. This remarkable story has been
told many times, in many books, and in many
languages. It has found its way into many modern dictionaries and grave encyclopædias, but
it always appears with an unsatisfactory and sus-
picious flavor. Dr Zach's ' discovery' is found
cropping up all over the continent, and everywhere is made paramount to Hariot's papers,
while Oxford is blamed for not giving the young
German his dues!

It seems that Dr Zach, a young man, was
in England with Count Bruhl, who had married

the dowager Lady Egremont. He thus had easy
access to the old Percy Library at Petworth, in
Sussex, where was stored, as we have seen by
Hariot's will, the black trunk containing his mathematical writings as bequeathed to the 9th Earl
of Northumberland. In 1785 Dr Zach announc-
ed with a truly scholastic flourish in Bode's Berlin Ephemeris for 1788 his remarkable ' discovery' of the papers of Thomas Hariot pre-
viously known as an eminent Algebraist or Mathematician, but now elevated to the rank also
of a first-class English Astronomer. The next
year, 1786, is celebrated in the annals of English science from the circumstance of Oxford's
having accepted a proposition from Dr Zach to
publish his account of Hariot and his writings.
The Royal Academy of Brussels in 1788 printed in its Memoirs Dr Zach's paper on the planet
Uranus, with a long note relative to the discovery at Petworth.

The Berlin paper immediately upon publication was translated into English and extensively
circulated in this country, conducing, it is sus-

pected, more to the renown of Dr Zach than to
that of Hariot. In 1793 Bode's Jahrbuch gave
from the pen of Dr Zach an account of the
Comets of 1607 and 1618, with Hariot's Observations thereon. But these observations were
given with so many errors and misreadings, as
shown by Professor Rigaud, that they were soon
pronounced worthless, to the discredit of Hariot
rather than of his eminent editor. But matters
came to a crisis in 1794, nine years after the
grand flourish of the first announcement at Berlin. Dr Zach sent to Oxford for publication
his abstract of certain of the scientific papers,
and the Earl of Egremont intrusted to the
University Dr Zach's selection of the original
papers. Zach's abstracts were merely sufficient
to identify himself with the works of Hariot, but
he had performed no real editorial labours, and
had not 'pen'd the doctrine' contained in them.
Here were years of useful work to be done which
the University dreamed not of, so the whole matter was referred to Professors Robertson and
Powell, who both reported adversely in 1798,

or before. In 1799 all the Hariot papers were returned to Petworth.

In the mean time the full translation of Dr Zach's account of his 'discovery,' with some curious additions, found its way into Dr Hutton's Dictionary of Mathematics, under Hariot, 1796, 2 volumes in quarto.   This publication gave an air of solemn record and history to the transactions, insomuch that Oxford began to be blamed for withholding from the press Dr Zach's great work. Oxford preserved a becoming silence. In 1803 Dr Zach published at Gotha in his Monatliche Correspondenz a fragment of that remarkable letter from the Earl of Northumberland to Hariot (which letter we have shown to be Lower's, see p. 120).   This publication, together with the reprint of the original Berlin paper by Zach in the second edition of Hutton's Dictionary in 1815 without alteration, seemed to bring the matter to a point.   Oxford was obliged to rise and explain.

The whole question was inquired into. Professor Robertson's original report was brought

out and sent to Dr David Brewster, who printed
it in his Edinburgh Philosophical Journal for
1822, volume vi, page 314, in an article on the
Hariot papers. In the meanwhile, in 1810, that
portion of the Hariot papers that did not go to
Oxford was presented to the British Museum
by the Earl of Egremont. The division of the
papers (on what principle it is difficult to guess)
was unquestionably Dr Zach's. The value is
no doubt much depreciated by the separation.
Under all these circumstances no one can wonder
at the Oxford decision, or that the papers were
deemed not worthy of publication. Yet under
other circumstances it is almost certain that
the two collections when worked together will
yield valuable materials for the life of Hariot
and the history and progress of English science,
discovery, and invention. To Professor S. F.
Rigaud is due the credit for the most part of
working out the crooked and entangled history
of the Zachean fiasco, which has apparently depreciated the real value of these papers. Professor Rigaud's papers may be seen in the Royal

Institution Journal, 1831, volume ii, pages 267-
271, in the Proceedings of the Royal Society,
iii, 125, and in the App[x] to Bradley's Works.

Now to pick up a few dropped stitches. Notices of Hariot by Camden, Aubrey, Hakewill,
and others are omitted from press of matter.
Gabriel Harvey in 1593, in his 'Pierces Super-
erogation,' page 190, exclaims 'and what pro-
founde Mathematician like Digges, Hariot, or
Dee esteemeth not the pregnant Mechanician ?'
Mr J.O. Halliwell's Collection of Letters referred
to on page 174, though falling late under our
eye, is most acceptable and thankfully used. Several letters of Sir William Lower are printed
from the originals in the British Museum. And
so is John Bulkley's dedication to Hariot of his
work on the Quadrature of the Circle, dated Kal.
Martii, 1591, the original manuscript of which
is in Sion College. There is also an interesting
letter from Hariot to the Earl dated Sion June
13, 1619, respecting the doctrine of reflections
as communicated to Warner and Hues for the
use of the Earl. But the most important letter

is the following on page 71 from Sir Thomas Aylesbury, one of Hariot's executors, to the Earl of Northumberland, respecting some remuneration for the extra services of Warner in assisting him in passing Hariot's ' Artis Analyticæ Praxis ' through the press :

R⁴ Ho.   May it plese your lõp.   July 5, 1632.

I presumed heretofore to moue your lõp on the behalf of Mr. W. for some consideration to be had of his extraordinary expense in attending the publication of Mr. H. book after the copy was finished. The same humble request I am induced to renew by reson of his present wants occasioned by that attendance.

For his literary labour and paines taken in forming the work and fitting it for the publik view, he looks for no other reward then your lõps acceptance therof as an honest discharge of his duty. But his long attendance through vnexpected difficulties in seeking to get the book freely printed, and after that was vndertaken the friuolous delaies of the printers and slow proceding of the presse, wᶜʰ no intreties of his or myne could remedy, drew him to a gretter expence then his meanes would bere, including both your lõps pencion and the arbitrary help of his frends. It is this extraordinary expense, wᶜʰ he cannot recouer wᶜʰ makes both him and me for him appele to your Lõps goodnes and bounty for some tollerable mitigation thereof.

I purpose God willing to set forth other peeces of Mr. H. wherein by reson of my owne incombrances I must of necessitie desire the help of Mr. W. rather then of any other, whereto I find him redy enough because it tends to your lõps service, and may the more freely trouble him, yf he receive some little encouragement from your lõp towards the repairing of the detrement that lies still vpon him by his last imploiment. But for the future my intention is to haue the impression at my owne

a a

charge, and not depend on the curtesy of those mechaniks, making account that wch may seeme to be saued by the other way will not countervaile the trouble and tedious prolongation of the busines.   But the copies being made perfect and faire written for the presse they shall be sufficiently bound to deliuer the books perfectly clen out of theire hands, and by this meanes the trouble and charge of attending the presse will be saued. Therfore my Lo. what you do now will be but for this once, and in such proportion as shall best like you to favour the humble motion of him who is

Allway most redy at your Lōps commaund   T. A.

Endorsed in the handwriting of Warner,

S^r Th. A. letters about my busines.

[B. M. Birch, 4396, 87.]

Notwithstanding the plain initials T. A. Mr Halliwell erroneously attributes this letter to Torporley, who had been in his grave three months. The handwriting is not Torporley's but Warner's. The Earl died on the 5th of November following. T. A. unquestionably stands for Sir Thomas Aylesbury, who, as executor and good friend, had the matter in hand. Indeed Warner's endorsement settles the question of authorship.

Six shillings and eight pence were paid for Hariot's knell, and £4 were paid as his legacy to the parish for the poor, according to memoranda supplied by Mr Edwin Freshfield from the Records of St Christopher's. See Will, page 200.

Hariot had a lease from Raleigh of ' Pinford grounds,' at Sherburne, for fifty-eight years, but the King wanted it for Carr, so of course the title was found defective.

In conclusion, before laying down the pen with which has been exhumed and set up on a new pedestal one of England's worthiest of her many forgotten Worthies, let the holder crave the indulgence of the reader for the illogical, wordy and mixed style of this essay. He is perfectly aware of these shortcomings, but puts in the plea that while groping in the past as if blindfolded he has been decoyed on step by step by the unexpected recovery of new materials after the others were in type, so that as often as he had finished his labor of love new facts have turned up which he had not the heart to reject. So he has incorporated them one after another as best he could. The results are more inartistic and crude than he could have wished, but he hesitates not on that account to invite lovers of and believers in the Truth of History to the banquet he has prepared.

A well-dined Reader is not likely, the writer thinks, to quarrel with his dessert because he has to pick out, with some little patience, the dainty meats of the nuts he has to arrange and crack for himself. Repetition, and perhaps some contradiction, are acknowledged. But meandering thoughts and ill-digested narratives, though tedious, are not criminal. When these new materials have dried in the noon-day sun for a year and a day, the writer then, or at the expiration of the Horatian period, may bring them back to his anvil to be re-hammered. May they then prove as true as they now seem new, is the wish of the admirer of Thomas Hariot, the first historian of Virginia, the friend of Sir Walter Raleigh, the companion of Henry Percy, and the Benefactor of Mankind.

The WILL of THOMAS HARIOT

Recorded in the Archdeaconry Court of London

 N THE NAME OF
God Amen y[e] nine and
twentieth daie of June, in
the yeare of o[r] Lord God
1621 And in y[e] yeares
of the reigne of o[r] Soue-
raigne Lord James by the
Grace of God of England
Scotland Fraunce & Ireland Kinge Defender
of the Faythe &[c] (that is to saie) of England
Fraunce & Ireland the nineteenth And of Scotland the fower & fiftieth I THOMAS HAR-
RIOTT of Syon in the County of Midd Gen-

tleman being troubled in my bodie wth infirmities. But of pfecte minde & memorie Laude
& prayse be giuen to Almightie God for the
same doe make & ordayne this my last will and
testam^t. In manner and forme following (vizt)
First & principally I Comitte my Soule in to
the hands of Almighty God my maker and of
his sonne Jesus Christe my Redeemer of whose
merritts by his grace wrought in mee by the holy
Ghoste I doubte not but that I am made ptaker,
to thend that I may enioye the Kingdome of
heaven ppared for the electe. Item my will is
that if I die in Londñ that my bodie bee in-
terred in the same pishe Churche of the house
where I lye the wch I Comitte to the discrecōn
of my Executors hereafter named, Excepte taking the advise and direccōn of the right honorable my very good Lord the EARLE OF NORTHUM-
BERLAND if it bee his pleasure to haue me bu-
ryed at Ilseworth in ye County of Midd And
if it be the pleasure of God that I die at Syon
I doe ordayne that my buriall bee at ye said
Churche of Ilseworth w^tout question Item I will
& bequeath vnto the aforesaid Earle One wooden
Boxe full or neere full of drawne Mappes standing nowe at the Northeast windowe of that Roome

wch is Called the plo^r at my house in Syon, And
if it pleaseth his Lor^{pp} to haue anie other Mappes
or Chartes drawne by hand or printed Or anie
Bookes or other thinges that I haue I desire my
Ex^{tors} that hee may haue them according to his
pleasure at reasonable rates excepte my Mathematicall papers in anie other sorte then is here after menconed Excepting alsoe some other thinges
giuen away in Legacies hereafter alsoe specified
𝕴tem I bequeath vnto the right honorable S^r
ROBERT SYDNEY KNIGHT VICOUNT LISLE,
One Boxe of papers being nowe vppon the table
in my Library at Syon, conteyning fiue quires
of paper, more or lesse wch were written by the
last Lord Harrington, and Coppyed out of some
of my Mathematicall papers for his instruccon
Alsoe I doe acknowledge that I haue two newe
greate globes wch haue Cou^s of Leather the w^{ch}
I borrowed of the said LORD LISLE And my will
is that they bee restored vnto him againe 𝕴tem
I giue vnto JOHN PROTHEROE of Hawkesbrooke
in the Countie of Carmarthen Esquier One furnace wth his apputnce out of the North Clossett
of my Library at Syon. 𝕴tem I giue vnto NATH-
ANIELL THORPERLEY of Salwarpe in the Countie
of Worcester Clarke One other furnace wth his

appūtñncꝑ out of the same Clossett. ⁋tem I giue vnto my servaunte Christopher Tooke one other furnace wᵗʰ his appūteñncꝑ out of the same Clossett Alsoe I giue to him an other furnace out of the South Clossett of my said Lybrarie ⁋tem I give and bequeath vnto Mʳⁱˢ Buckner wife vnto Thomas Buckner Mercer at whose house being in Sᵗ Christophers pishe I nowe lye, and hereafter nominated one of my Executors the some of fifteene poundes towards the repacōns of some damages that I haue made, or for other vses as shee shall thincke Convenient ⁋tem I giue vnto Mʳ John Buckner theire eldest sonne the some of fiue poundes ⁋tem I giue & bequeath vnto my Cozen Thomas Yates my sisters sonne fifty poundes towardes the paiemᵗ. of his debtꝑ and not otherwise, But if his debtꝑ doe fall out to be lesse then fifty poundes then the residue to remayne to himselfe ⁋tem to John Harriottꝑ Late servaunte to Mʳ Doleman of Shawe neere Newbury in Barkeshire and being the sonne of my vnckle John Harriottꝑ but nowe married and dwelling in Churche peene about a Myle west-ward from the said Shawe, I doe giue and bequeath fifty poundes ⁋tem I giue and bequeath vnto Christopher Tooke my fore said servaunte one

hundred poundes. Item I giue & bequeath vnto
my servaunte JOHN SHELLER fiue poundes more
then the forty shillinges wch I haue of his in Cus-
todie, being moneygiven vnto him at seƲall tymes
by my frends wch in all is seauen poundes to bee
imployed for his vse according to the discretōn
of my Executors for ye placing of him wth an
other Master Item I giue and bequeath to JOANE
my servaunte fiue poundes more then her wages.
Item I giue and bequeath vnto my s̄vaunte
JANE wch serveth vnder the said JONE fortie shillinges more then her wages wch wages is twenty
shillinges by yeare Item I giue and bequeath
to my auncient s̄vaunte CHRISTOPHER KELLETT
a Lymning paynter dwelling neare Petty Fraunce
in Westminster fiue poundes Item to my ain-
cient servaunte JOANE wife to Paule Chapman
dwelling in Brayneford end I bequeath fortie
shillinges. Item I giue vnto the aforesaid
EARLE OF NORTHUMBERLAND my two pspectiue trunckes wherew^th I vse espetially to see
Venus horned like the Moone and the Spottꝑ
in the Sonne The glasses of wch trunckes I desire to haue remooved into two other of the
fayrest trunckes by my said servaunte CHRIS-
TOPHER TOOKE Item I bequeath vnto euy one

b b

of my Executors hereafterwards to be named,
One pspectiue truncke a peece of the best glasses,
and yᵉ fayrest trunckes, as my said servaunte
Can best fitt to theire liking 𝕵𝖙𝖊𝖒 I giue vnto
my said servaunte CHRISTOPHER TOOKE the
residue of my Cases of pspectiue trunckes wᵗʰ
the other glasses of his owne making fitted for
pspectiue trunckes (excepting two great longe
trunckes Consisting of many ptes wᶜʰ I giue
vnto the said EARLE OF NORTHUMBERLAND to
remayne in his Library for such vses as they
may be put vnto, Alsoe I bequeath the dishes
of iron Called by the spectacle makers tooles to
grinde spectacles, and other pspectiue glasses for
trunckes vnto my foresaid servaunte CHRISTO-
PHER TOOKE, 𝕵𝖙𝖊𝖒 Concerninge my debts, I
doe acknowledg that at this psente I doe owe
moneyes to Monseir Mayornes a Potycarie
More to Mʳ Wheately a Potticary dwelling
neare the Stockes at the East end of Cheapeside
𝕵𝖙𝖊𝖒 to my Brewer dwelling at Braynford
end, 𝕵𝖙𝖊𝖒 to Mʳ John Bill Staꞔoner for
Bookes The some of the debtꝑ to all fower
before menꞔoned I thincke and Judge not to bee
much more or lesse then forty poundes. 𝕵𝖙𝖊𝖒
I doe acknowledge to owe vnto Mʳ Christo-

pher Ingram keeper of the house of Syon for the
aforesaid EARLE OF NORTHUMBERLAND Three
thousand six hundred of Billettꝭ wᶜʰ I desire
to be repayed vnto him 𝕴𝖙𝖊𝖒 I doe acknowledge that I haue some written Coppies to the
number of twelue or fowerteene (more or lesse)
lent vnto me by Thomas Allen of Gloster
Hall in Oxford Mʳ of Artes vnto whome I desire my Executors hereafter named to restore
them safely according to the noate that hee shall
deliũ of them (I doubting whether I haue anie
true noate of them my selfe) 𝕴𝖙𝖊𝖒 I make
Constitute and ordayne theise fowre following
my Executors Namely the aforesaid Sʳ ROBERT
SIDNEY KNIGHT VISCOUNT LYSLE (if his LOᴾᴾ
may take soe many paynes in my behalfe) Also
JOHN PROTHEROE of Hawkesbrooke in the
County of Carmarthen Esquioʳ Alsoe THOMAS
ALESBURY of Westminster Esquior Lastly
THOMAS BUCKNER Mercer dwelling in Sᵗ
Xꝓofers ꝑishe in Lonᵈ not farre from yᵉ Royall
Exchainge vnto wᶜʰ Executors I giue full power
& aucty to vse theire owne discreꝬons in paying
theire Charges in my behalfe out of the rest of
my goodꝭ And if my Bookes wᵗʰ other goods
doe in value Come to more then I haue afore

supposed First I desire them to bestowe soe
much vppon yᵉ poore not exceeding twenty
poundes as they shall thincke Convenient sofñe
p̃te whereof I giue vnto the poore of the hospi-
tall in Christes Churche in Lonđ, Some p̃te
vnto the said p̃ishe of Sᵗ X p̃ofors where I nowe
lye, and some p̃te wᶜʰ I would haue the greater)
vnto the poore of the p̃ishe of Isleworth neere
Syon in the Countie of Miđd Secondly out of
the said residue of my goodẽ, my will is, That
the said Executors take some p̃te thereof for
theire owne vses according to theire discretions
Lastly my will and desire is that they bestowe
the value of the rest vppon Sʳ Thomas Bodleyes
Library in Oxford, or imploy it to such Charitable & pious vses as they shall thincke best
𝕴𝕥𝕰𝕸 my will and desire is that Robert Hughes
gentleman and nowe attendant vppon th'afore
said Earle of Northumberland for matters of Learning bee an ofñseer at the prizing of
my Bookes, and some other thinges as my Executors and hee shall agree vnto 𝕴𝕥𝕰𝕸 I ordayne and Constitute the aforesaid Nathaniell
Thorperley first to be Ofñseer of my Mathematicall Writinges to be receiued of my Executors to p̃vse and order and to sep̃ate the Cheife

of them from my waste papers, to the end that
after hee doth vnderstand them hee may make
vse in penninge such doctrine that belonges vnto
them for publique vses as it shall be thought
Convenient by my Executors and him selfe
And if it happen that some manner of Notacōns
or writinges of the said papers shall not be vn-
derstood by him then my desire is that it will
please him to Conferre wth Mr Warner or M^r
Hughes Attendants on the aforesaid Earle Concerning the aforesaid doubte. And if hee be
not resolued by either of them That then hee
Conferre wth the aforesaid JOHN PROTHEROE
Esquior or the aforesaid THOMAS ALESBURY
Esquior. (I hoping that some or other of the
aforesaid fower last nominated can resolue him)
And when hee hath had the vse of the said
papers soe longe as my Executors and hee have
agreed for the vse afore said That then he de-
liū them againe vnto my Executors to be putt
into a Convenient Truncke with a locke &
key and to be placed in my Lord of Northumberlandes Library and the key thereof to be de-
liūed into his Lord^{pps} hands And if at anie tyme
after my Executors or the afore said NATH-
ANIELL THORPERLEY shall agayne desire the

vse of some or all of the said Mathematicall
paps That then it will please the said Earle to
lett anie of the aforesaid to haue them for theire
vse soe long as shall be thought Convenient,
and afterwards to be restored agayne vnto the
Truncke in the afore said Earle's Library
Secondly my will & desire is that the said
Nathaniell Thorperley be alsoe Ouseere
of other written bookes & papers as my Executors and hee shall thincke Convenient. Item
Whereas I haue diuers waste papers (of w^{ch}
some are in a Canvas bagge) of my Accompt̃ to
Sr Walter Rawley for all wch I haue discharges
or acquitances lying in some boxes or other my
desire is that they may bee all burnte. Alsoe
there is an other Canvas bagge of papers concerning Irishe Accompt̃ (the psons whome they
Concerne are dead many yeares since in the
raigne of queene Elizabeth wch I desire alsoe
may be burnte as likewise many Idle paps and
Cancelled Deedes wch are good for noe vse
Item I revoake all former will̃ by mee heretofore made saue onely this my p̃nte last will
and Testament wch I will shalbe in all thinges
effectually and truely pformed according to the
tenor and true meaning of the same In wit-

nes whereof I the afore said THOMAS HARRIOTTℓ
haue to this my p̃sent last will & Testament put
my hand & seale yeouen the daie and yeare first
aboue written   THO : HARRIOTTS.

Sealed published and deliũed by yᵉwᵗʰin named
THOMAS HARRIOTTℓ for and as his last will &
Testamᵗ the daie & yeares wᵗʰin written in the
p̃fice of vs IMMANUELL BOWRNE WILL : FUT-
TER, Scr : & THO : ALFORD Svᵗᵉ to the said scr̃ :

Probatum fuit hm̃oi Testũm sexto die
mensis Julij Anno Dñi 1621. Coram venˡⁱ viro
RICHARDO CLARKE legum Dc̃ore Surᵗᵒ Dñi
Offitis &ᶜ. Jurᵗᵒ THOME AILESBURIE et THOME
BUCKNER duorum Exĩorum &ᶜ quibus &ᶜ de
bene &ᶜ saluo Jure &ᶜ Resr̃vata tamen p̃ate
similem Com̃issionem faciendi Dño ROBERTO
SIDNEY militi et JOHANNI PROTHERO armigero
alteris Ex̃toribus &ᶜ Cum venerint eandem in
debita Juris forma petituri. Pro Invenᵒ ANDREE
prox̃ &ᶜ. Concordat cum Originali fc̃a exaĩacoe
p̃nos HEN : DURHAM Noʳⁱᵘᵐ Pubᶜᵐ RA : BYRDE

[From the certified copy filed in the Probate Registry in
Somerset House, which has been collated with the copy re-
gistered, Arch. Lond. 1618—1626/7, Folio 71. The differences
in spelling, punctuation etc. are numerous but unimportant.]

END

INDEX TO LIFE OF THOMAS HARIOT.

C C

BIBLIOGRAPHY